Girl in a Red River Coat

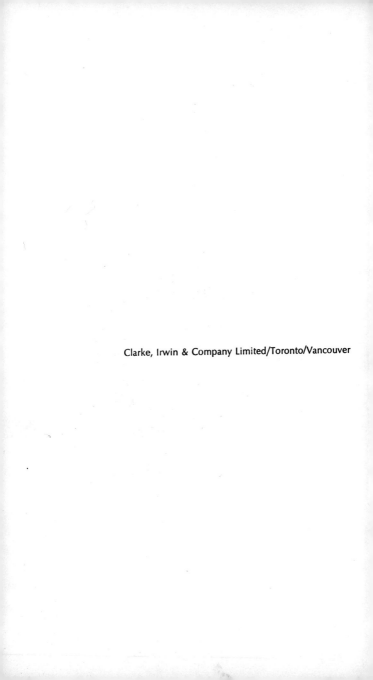

Clarke, Irwin & Company Limited/Toronto/Vancouver

Girl in a Red River Coat

MARY PEATE

© 1970 by Clarke, Irwin & Company Limited

First printed in paperback format 1973

ISBN 0-7720-0595-8

Printed in Canada

1 2 3 4 5 JD 77 76 75 74 73

For my daughter, Candice Mary,
with love

Contents

"We were somewhere in North Africa when we heard a dull, distant crash that echoed to the farthest wastes of the desert.

'What was that?'

'Did you hear it?'

'It was nothing.'

'Do you think we ought to go . . . and see?'

'No — it was nothing.' "

F. Scott Fitzgerald, *My Lost City*

"I was born in that wonderful year — 1929."

Jackie Vernon, *A Wet Bird Never Flies at Night*

Girl in a Red River Coat

Run, Sheep, Run

The morning after my aunt came to live with us, my friend Margaret phoned to see what I felt like doing, and I took the phone into the dining-room closet so my aunt wouldn't overhear.

Not that anything we had to say was worth eavesdropping on. After tossing a few ideas back and forth, we decided to take some sandwiches to Westmount Park for a picnic. I said I figured I could sneak an empty milk bottle out of the flat to cash in, and Margaret said she had a cent, so we'd be able to get something to drink with the sandwiches. After discussing whether to squander the money on a bottle of Cherry Jumbo, a bottle of Kik, or two three-cent bottles of Flirt, we decided in favour of the Kik because you got more.

As it happened, when I went to get the milk bottle my mother was busy with my aunt, so I took two, which meant

1

that along with the bottle of Kik we could get five cents worth of cent candy.

The screen door on the candy store had a bell rigged to it, which jangled each time someone entered. Mr. Meyer, the owner of the store, always looked hopefully toward the door at the sound of the bell, but when he saw it was only Margaret and me his expression turned to one of resignation.

I had been patronizing his store since we'd moved to Nôtre Dame de Grace, and, though he didn't try to conceal his lack of interest in my trade, I continued to take him my steady custom. Our relationship was based on a firm foundation of mutual distrust.

Setting the empty bottles down on top of the soft drink cooler, I said, "Will you give me cash for these bottles please, Mr. Meyer?"

He eyed the bottles suspiciously. "Did you get the milk here, Mary?"

"Oh yes, Mr. Meyer," I rushed to assure him. ". . . I mean my brother did."

Looking sceptical, Meyer rang up NO SALE on the cash register, and handed me two nickels. I pulled out a cold, wet bottle of Kik from the cooler, handed him back one of the nickels, Margaret gave him her penny, and then we moved down toward the back of the store to stand in front of the cent candy display. He moved down too, and took his stand behind the case, waiting for us to make up our minds.

He must have worn a groove in the floor behind the counter, waiting for kids to make up their minds. But it was his own fault for setting out such a tempting, mouth-watering display.

How could anyone be expected to make up her mind quickly when faced with such confections? Chocolate-covered coconut balls; chocolate-covered, molasses-flavoured, oval-shaped honeymoons; little licorice pipes with tiny red candies stuck to the bowl, looking as if they were all lit, ready to be smoked; wax false teeth the "gums" of which were filled with a pink, delicious liquid which flavoured the wax when you chewed it; tiny wax bottles filled with coloured liquids; miniature cones full of syrup and candy "ice cream"; candy buttons on paper;

sponge candy; licorice whips, both red and black; grab bags. . . ."

"Any good stuff in the grab bags today, Mr. Meyer?" I asked.

He shrugged. "Isn't there always?"

"My father says you just put junk in the grab bags. Is that true, Mr. Meyer?"

He made no reply, but directed a "Why me, Lord?" glance heavenward. I pressed on.

"My father says the prizes in the grab bags are junk too. I got a gold ring in a grab bag once. And it turned my finger green. And then my finger began to swell. And I couldn't get the ring off. And then my father had to borrow a saw and saw the ring off."

"Do me a favour," Meyer interrupted. "Don't get a grab bag."

After I'd made up my mind, with Margaret's help, I handed him back the other nickel he'd given me, and as he took it he muttered to the invisible companion he was always talking to. "Hoo . . . the last of the big time spenders."

As we started our walk along Sherbrooke St. to Westmount Park, I told Margaret about my aunt, beginning by yawning elaborately.

"I didn't get much sleep last night."

"How come?"

"My aunt woke me in the middle of the night."

"Why?"

"Because she was crying so loud."

"What was she crying for?"

"I don't know. I guess because she's sick."

"What's wrong with her?"

"My mother says she had a stroke."

"What's that?"

"I don't know exactly, but that's what my mother says she had. When she came into the flat yesterday, she walked funny. She can't move her fingers properly, either."

"How did she get here?"

3

"Her brother and his son brought her. She had to hold on to both of them when she came in."

"That's too bad."

"She used to teach music in Toronto and now she can't play the piano or teach or anything."

"Is that why she was crying?"

"I guess so. My mother says she's had a very sad life. She used to be married a long time ago and her husband was mean to her and she wanted to leave him and he wouldn't let her because they had this little boy. But my aunt wanted to get away from her husband so bad, she told him he could have the little boy. And she's been sorry ever since."

"Couldn't her little boy come to see her?"

"He's not a little boy now. He must be a man. But she doesn't know where he is even. She hasn't seen him since she left her husband, and he was only eight years old then. I think she promised her husband she wouldn't try to see the boy if he would leave her alone."

"What did he used to do to her?"

"I don't know. I asked my mother and she said he was very jealous. Before she taught music she used to travel around playing the piano in theatres and concert halls and her husband didn't like it. He didn't like the people she met and worked with either. I heard my mother telling my big sister once that when he had his jealous fits he used to accuse my aunt of doing all sorts of things she really didn't do."

"What sorts of things?"

"I don't know. She didn't say. Anyway it sure was spooky hearing her cry like that. It wasn't like ordinary crying at all. It was high and sort of—eeeeee—like that. It made me feel sick to my stomach. I hate that kind of crying. I hate having her live with us. She's got my bedroom and I have to sleep in the living room. I hate *her*."

"It's a sin to hate somebody," Margaret said.

I looked at her sharply to see how come all of a sudden she was such a Miss Pious Pockets, as my father would say. She, a Protestant, who only went to Sunday school and church once a week, was telling me, a Catholic, about sin—as if

4

Catholics didn't know more about sin than anybody.

"If you hate somebody, you hate them," I said. "I can't help it if it's a sin."

"You're supposed to love everybody. Or at least if you can't love them, you're supposed to like them," she said primly.

"But how can you like somebody if you *don't* like them?" I demanded.

"It doesn't matter. Our minister says you're supposed to love thy neighbour as thyself."

Her minister. As if I didn't practically know the entire Sermon on the Mount by heart. As if I didn't know the six precepts of the church, the seven deadly sins, the eight beatitudes, the ten commandments, and all those other things in my catechism, and she was telling me.

"Well," I told her, in as scathing a tone as I could summon, "That's all right for you to say. You don't have thy neighbour sleeping in thy bed."

After we'd eaten our lunch in the park, we put the left-overs into a bag and went into the Conservatory to see the flowers and huge goldfish that swam in the lily pond there. When no one was looking, we fed our leftover slices of baloney to the goldfish, who gobbled them up with bon appétit.

After that, we went next door to Westmount Library to look through the books in the children's section. We couldn't take them out because we weren't Westmount residents, but we were allowed to sit at the tables and read them, so we each chose a book of short stories set in a British girls' boarding school.

I really loved those books. The girls in the stories all had names like Hilary, Pamela, Gwendolyn and Cynthia. Pamela, the rich girl, was generally described as an "absolute brick," and poor Hilary was always being "sent to Coventry," which meant that no one would speak to her. The misdeed that would incur the wrath of the entire school might have been Hilary's seemingly deliberate losing of the field hockey match to St. Swithins; or being responsible for their being caught after "lights out" eating "sweets," "creams" and "sticky buns."

5

Such an adventure usually involved the entire student body, and a singularly unattractive student body it was. The illustrations depicted flat-chested girls with wrinkled black stockings, serge tunics belted somewhere around the knees, and short, frizzy hair-dos.

On the way home, Margaret and I talked in clipped accents we fancied sounded British, and when we got to the corner of our street we stopped by the drugstore to try them out on the proprietor.

"I say, old chap," I said. "Have you any free samples today?"

"Not today girls," he said.

"Oh. Teddibley sorry to bother you. Toodle-pip then," we said, and left.

He usually had something for us—tiny tubes of toothpaste, miniature bottles of perfume or little tubes of Tangee lipstick.

The best things to get were samples of cough drops, which you could eat in school and the teacher couldn't say anything because she couldn't be sure you weren't trying to ease a sore throat. If you were caught chewing gum you had to stick it on the end of your nose and go from classroom to classroom to be laughed at—a punishment my father said was a sin against human dignity—but cough drops were tolerated.

From the drugstore we crossed over to see our friend Arnold, who managed the grocery store at the corner of our street. We didn't try out our English accents on him, because he was always putting on accents for us.

"Faith, and what can I do for you two colleens today?" he greeted us. Because he'd called us colleens, I knew he was supposed to be Irish.

"Have you got any orange crates, Arnold?" I asked.

"And what would youse be wantin' with orange crates, if yuz don't mind me askin'?"

"We thought we'd paint them and make doll houses out of them."

"Sure an' that's a foin idea. Me own colleens do the same thing. I'll go and see what I've got fur yuz."

Margaret and I couldn't help laughing.

"And whot's so funny, please?" he asked.

"Gee Arnold," I said. "That's the worst Irish accent I ever heard."

"How can yuz be sayin' a terrible thing like that to someone from the old sod?" he asked, looking aggrieved as he went out to the back of the store. When he returned, he was carrying an orange crate in each hand.

"Gee, thanks a lot Arnold," I said.

"Ya, thanks," Margaret said, reaching to take one from him.

"Ah tut-tut-tut. These are for gairls who appreciate me Irish brogue, not for the likes of you spalpeens."

"Aw come on Arnold," I said. "I was only fooling."

"You're sure?"

"Yes," Margaret said. "You really sound just like Ajax Cassidy."

"Weeeeeel that's better. Alright then. Here you are—two of the foinest doll houses in N.D.G. But don't go broadcasting it around where yuz got them, you hear?"

"We won't," we promised, and, picking up the cumbersome crates, staggered under the bulk of them out of the store.

By the time we reached home it was four o'clock, and time to get all cleaned up for supper. My aunt was having a bath, with the assistance of my mother, in our only bathroom, so I had to wait, impatiently, to have mine.

Most of the little girls on the street went through this getting "all cleaned up" ritual. Then, after we'd had our baths, with our hair brushed, and dressed in fresh, clean dresses with our foreheads gleaming and scalps smarting, we were sent out again and cautioned under penalty of death not to get dirty before our fathers came home.

In order to preserve our "all saucered and blown" appearance, as my father described it, we would usually sit on somebody's front steps and talk.

The older girls always congregated on the steps directly across the street from us, and wouldn't let us join them because they said we were too young to hear what they were saying.

That afternoon, however, because we'd had such a successful day and I was feeling lucky, I suggested to Margaret that we try to crash the *élite* party across the way.

7

As we approached, Nancy said to the other girls in an unnecessarily loud voice, "Better stop talking now. Here come the babies."

"Oh you think you're so big," Margaret said, not even trying for an ingratiating opening gambit.

"We know a lot more than you. You don't know about anything," Nancy said.

"Whadaya mean?" I asked.

"Bet you don't even know where babies come from," she said snottily.

"I do so."

"Where?"

I thought back to the very first exchange in our catechism which went: QUESTION: Who made you? ANSWER: God made me.

"From God," I answered, trying to keep the note of triumph out of my voice.

They burst into raucous laughter.

"Well I know they come out of their mother's stomach," I said defensively.

"Everybody knows *that*. But who puts them there?" Nancy prodded.

I would've answered God again if it hadn't gotten such a big laugh before. Would they believe the Holy Ghost? I remained silent.

"See—you don't know."

"Well who *does* put them there then?"

They told me. Graphically. Practically with coloured slides. I didn't believe a word of it.

"It's true," they insisted. "All babies are started that way."

A bell rang and an electric light bulb went on over my head. I remembered something. . . .

"*Catholic* babies aren't," I told them.

"Oh, yes they are," they assured me.

The concepts of the Virgin Birth and the Immaculate Conception were hazy in my mind because the nuns and priests always glossed over them quickly, but there was something about the Holy Ghost and the Blessed Virgin. . . .

"Jesus wasn't started that way," I told them, not even trying to hide my triumph this time.

"He was so. Catholics think His mother didn't do it, but she did."

"How do *you* know?"

"I know, that's all."

What was the point in arguing? After all, what did *I* know? No one had ever told me anything, and I had only had one experience with sex. That had been when I was six years old and a bunch of boys and girls on our street had been playing doctor behind the Milligan's flat.

Mrs. Milligan had come out and found us and her face had been a mask of disapproval as she made us all sit down while she talked to us. She told us that what we had been doing was wicked and sinful, and, when she spied me cowering in a corner, she singled me out for special attention because I was the only Catholic in the group. She said she was shocked to see that a little Catholic girl would take part in such a nasty pastime, and reminded me that I would have to tell about it when I made my First Confession.

I didn't understand why the fact that I was a Catholic should make me less fascinated by what Norman had that I didn't, but what she said worried me for the next year till I made my First Confession. There were many nights when I awoke in a sweat, wondering how I could phrase the act for the priest. I wondered if he would know what was meant by the term "playing doctor," and, if he didn't, how I would articulate it for him.

When the time finally came and I reached the age of seven and was making my First Confession, I whispered the dread thing to the priest and he either didn't hear me, or pretended not to. At any rate, he didn't ask any questions, which was a relief.

So how could someone with such limited experience challenge an expert like Nancy? By the time she had finished giving us the facts, Margaret and I had managed to insinuate ourselves onto the bottom two steps, and while we sat there listening, Murray, a little Jewish boy who lived down the street, walked by. Nancy interrupted herself in a particularly erotic anecdote to call out to him, "Christ-killer!"

"Ya, Christ-killer!" Jan also took up the taunt, echoed by her sister Shirley.

Murray averted his face as he walked gamely past. You really had to admire his spunk for such a little kid. He neither looked in our direction nor gave any indication of having heard.

"What do you call him that for?" I asked Nancy.

"Because the Jews killed Christ, that's why."

"But *Murray* didn't," I protested. "He's only six years old."

"It doesn't matter," Nancy said darkly. She had minded Murray for his mother two or three years before and had always been taking down his pants to show us what he had. What he had wasn't as impressive as what Norman had. "Christ-killer!" she raised her voice again.

Perhaps everyone looks ugly when they're shouting, but it seemed to me that Nancy, Jan and Shirley looked particularly ugly with their mouths open, their eyes cold and their faces contorted.

A new voice was added to the chorus. Margaret had joined the group of shouters. Nancy was leading the chant now, and beckoned to me to join in. Could I risk losing status with the group I had so recently and precariously become a part of? I joined in.

My eyes followed Murray as he continued down the street. What I saw was a small boy with crisp, dark hair, short pants and a sleeveless jersey. His back seemed to stiffen perceptibly as the chorus increased in volume. We were really going great, when, for the first time I noticed the celluloid protector taped to his arm. It was there to cover the smallpox vaccination he'd had because he was starting school in September. The protector seemed to somehow make him more vulnerable, and, for some reason, I had a queasy feeling in my stomach after seeing it. I stopped shouting, and the muscles around my mouth seemed to be pulling down involuntarily, and I had trouble trying to control them.

All those things Nancy had said about what men and ladies

did; the shouting at Murray; and Murray's vaccination protector combined to make me sorry I had ever suggested to Margaret we try to join Nancy and her followers. Perhaps the older girls had been right. Maybe we *were* too young for their heady company.

After supper

After supper, my sister did the dishes and my mother helped my aunt set her hair—all this in preparation for the doctor's visit the next day—and my father gave me a nickel, so I went up to the candy store to get a Chily Bear.

As I walked back down the street eating it as slowly as possible, savouring particularly the orange sherbet in the centre of the vanilla ice cream, all around me were the jumble of sounds peculiar to the street in the early evening.

Some people had their radios on in their living rooms, and words and phrases from newscasts wafted from open windows. Names like Mayor Raynault, Premier Maurice Duplessis, and Prime Minister Mackenzie King mingled with the kid's chants as they played different games.

The kids who were playing Double-dutch sang things like:

Ice cream soda,
lemonade,
tart.
Tell me the name
of your sweet*heart*.

And,
Salt, mustard, vinegar, PEPPER!

And,
Mary had a baby.
His name was Sunny *Jim*.
She put him in the bathtub
to have a little *swim*.
He drank all the water.
He ate all the soap.
Mary called the doctor.
The doctor had no *hope*.

The kids who were playing "May I?" were being given intricate instructions like: "Barbara, you may take two and a half teentzy weentzy butterfly steps backwards."

And the kids who were bouncing lacrosse balls were chanting:

Have a cup of tea sir.
No sir.
Why sir?
Because I have a cold sir.
Where'd you get your cold sir?
Up in the north pole sir.
What were you doing there sir?
Catching polar bear sir.

And the kids who were trading insults called:

I see England
I see France
I see a hole
in Nancy's pants.

To which Nancy snidely replied, "Well they're clean, and all paid for."

And,

Sticks and stones
may break my bones
but names can never hurt me.

Then,

French pea soup and johnny cake
make a Frenchman's belly ache.

And,

"Vatant chez vous, maudit Anglais."

These last shouts were between some of the kids on our street and the only French-speaking kids on the block, who lived on the next street and sometimes ventured through the connecting lane.

I could feel a certain empathy with the French kids because I knew what it had been like to be a member of one of the few English-speaking families in a French-speaking neighbourhood.

This had been when we first came to Montreal from Mimico, the Toronto suburb where I was born. My father's friend, who had persuaded him to leave the Art Department of the Toronto *Telegram* for *The Montreal Star*, had found the flat for us before we moved, and it had been right in the heart of a French-speaking district.

I had only been four at the time, so it hadn't mattered to me where I lived, but the rest of the family, who were all older than I, felt as if they had come to live in a foreign country. All of the duplexes had winding circular outdoor staircases with black iron railings leading to the upper flats, which my mother's Ontario eyes couldn't become accustomed to; most of the neighbours spoke only French, and all of the tradesmen and storekeepers were unilingual too.

My mother had hoped I'd learn the language from my playmates, but it hadn't worked out that way. I played with a little girl named Denise, and within a few weeks she had learned to speak English from my four-year-old vocabulary.

The only French I learned was from the little boys who stood outside our backyard fence and shouted, "*Mange la merde*" and "*Maudit foule*" at me. I called these French phrases back to them, proud of my bilingualism.

After living in that French-speaking community for just a few months, my mother could no longer tolerate the isolation, so she looked for an English-speaking district for us to move to.

She and I took long bus and streetcar rides to various sections of the city, then got off the car and walked around, going into stores and asking passers-by directions. When she finally found a district where the rents were within her price range, that had indoor staircases, and where most of the shopkeepers and passers-by spoke English, she decided it was the spot for us, and without waiting for our lease to run out we moved to Nôtre Dame de Grace, more familiarly known as N.D.G.

It seemed as if we'd moved back to an English-speaking province. Except for the occasional exchange with the French-speaking kids on the next street, and a few tradespeople, we seldom heard the French language spoken, even though we were living in the second largest French-speaking city in the world.

After I finished my Chily Bear, I joined a game of Run, Sheep, Run, which was broken up when Nancy had to go in to listen to Uncle Troy, The Kiddies' Answer Man, played by Corey Thomson, and sponsored by Troy Laundries.

Every evening, just as we were engrossed in a game, Nancy's mother would come out on their balcony and call down, "Nancee. It's time for Uncle Troy." And Nancy would say, "Aw, can't I stay out five minutes more?" And her mother would say, "No, come in now." And Nancy would stamp her foot and whine, "Do I hafta?" And her mother would say, "Yes." So Nancy would get a lip on her and stomp up the stairs, muttering swear words in Pig Latin. She didn't seem too crazy about Uncle Troy.

Our sleeping arrangements since my aunt's arrival were that, when it was time for me to go to bed, I was put in my parents' room until their bedtime, then they would half-awaken me and guide me into the living room and onto the made-up couch. This arrangement had its compensations. Their bedroom was off the dining room, where the radio was, so I could lie awake and listen to it.

Our radio was a floor model with a slanting front and a green "magic eye" in its centre to register whether or not you had tuned in the station correctly. The eye had an almost human quality. If a lady in a play shrieked, the eye would blink rapidly. It would also protest gunfire, police sirens and opera singers.

The last voice I heard from the radio that night was Christopher Ellis reading the news. He had a rich, mellow voice that seemed to mellow appreciably when he spoke of the "long green bottles" of his sponsor's product, Molson's Ale. His newscast told about how the Japanese were fighting with the Chinese; the Italians were fighting with the Ethiopians; the Germans were fighting with the Austrians and the Spaniards were fighting with each other.

Not too different from our block, really.

Sitting on the front steps

The next morning, Margaret and I started working on our doll houses.

I found some pink paint in our basement and we used it to paint the orange crates. Margaret found some wood, so we used that to make balconies. I also came across some canvas while looking for the paint, so we divided it and made awnings, by hemming the edges, sticking wire through the hems and thumbtacking them over the balconies.

One thing about having my aunt living with us; while she was taking up my mother's attention I was free to do things she might not have permitted me to do, like taking the paint, and painting the boxes out on the front porch.

At one point during the morning, Margaret put down her paintbrush, and, wiping her hands on her shorts, said, "Come on. Here comes the iceman."

We jumped up and ran up to the ice wagon as it stopped in front of Mrs. Milligan's, stood awhile watching the iceman swing the huge chunks of ice off the back of the wagon; then Margaret said admiringly, "Wow! Imagine being able to lift fifty pounds in one hand!" Then, as the iceman gripped another block of ice with the tongs, causing showers of ice shards to fly up, Margaret said, "Whew! It's hot today."

The ice man was uncomprehending.

Margaret then pantomimed wiping her brow and said, "*Très chaude.*" So the iceman chipped off some pieces for us with the ice pick.

"*Merci,*" we said, and went back to the front steps to eat it. What a treat that ice was to the tongue and hands on a hot day! Mrs. Milligan had seen us eating it once, and told us we'd get hydrophobia because the ice had been lying in the wagon covered with sawdust and an oil-stained tarpaulin. But I had never heard of anyone getting hydrophobia from eating it. Anyway, as we sat on the steps licking the ice and feeling the cold water trickle down from our wrists to our elbows, we didn't worry too much about it.

Another taste treat we had that day was when the tar men came around to patch the roof of the apartment building across the street. They had a sort of cart with a portable furnace on it, and, when they melted the tar over the blazing fire, a wonderful smell permeated the neighbourhood. Margaret and I strolled over and got as close to the fire as possible.

"*Donnez-moi* some tar *s'il vous plaît*?" Margaret asked one of the men, holding out her hand, in case he didn't understand her French. The man handed her a soft, warm, pliable black blob, and we went back to the steps to divide and chew it.

After she had worked the tar to a chewy consistency, Margaret asked, "Do you believe chewing tar makes your teeth white?"

I said I thought it did, and the subject of beliefs and superstitions must've taken her fancy because she asked, "Do you believe about the inside of a golf ball? That if the stuff inside gets in your eyes you'll go blind?"

"I'm sure not going to try to find out," I told her.

"Do you believe," she went on, "that if you do this"—she rubbed her finger in an up and down motion on her teeth—"in front of a Chinaman, he'll chase you with a cleaver?"

"Well," I admitted, "whenever I pass the Chinese laundry on Sherbrooke St., just to be on the safe side, I always walk with my hands behind my back."

"Do you believe if you cut yourself here,"—she indicated the skin between her thumb and forefinger—"you'll get lock-jaw?"

"I think so," I said, then had a question of my own. "Do you believe if you look cross-eyed, your eyes will stay that way?"

"No," she said, and looked cross-eyed to prove it. I felt uneasy when she did it, and it seemed to me that afterward her eyes did turn in a little.

"Some people," I said, "think that if you drop a fork company is coming; or if you have bubbles in your tea you're going to get money; and if your nose itches you're going to kiss a fool; or, if your ears burn, somebody's talking about you; and, if you walk under a ladder, it's bad luck. . . ."

Margaret was nodding disdainfully all through my recital. "I know," she said, with an air of superiority, "and if you open an umbrella inside the house, it's bad luck; and if a black cat crosses your path, it's bad luck; and if you put a hat on a bed, it's bad luck; and if you break a mirror, it's seven years bad luck." She dismissed all these dreadful things with a wave of her hand. "My mother says it's Irish to believe all that stuff."

"You should hear what some of my teachers believe," I told her. "One of the nuns told us that on the last day of the world the St. Lawrence River is going to turn to blood, and all the sinners in Montreal are going to have to swim in it. Do you believe that?"

Margaret made a plosive, scoffing, derisive sound with her lips. "No, I don't believe it."

"Well *she* believes it."

"If you ask me, she must be a little . . .," Margaret waved her forefinger in a circle around her ear, significantly.

I made a confession. "One night I dreamed the St. Lawrence River really *had* turned to blood, and it was full of sinners, all swimming around. And then, all of a sudden, *I* was swimming in it too. Ugh! It was awful!"

Margaret paused in her tar-chewing and turned to look at me. "You must've *really* believed her."

"I guess so," I said. "But why would she tell us that if it isn't true?"

"Maybe she told you that so you'd be good—like when my mother used to tell me a bogey man would come and take me away if I wasn't good."

"Did your mother really tell you that?"

"Sure."

"I don't think it's nice to say something like that to a little kid."

At that point, Margaret looked up the street and said, "Here comes Mr. Hoover." We watched his uncertain progress down the street, and as he drew nearer, we chorused, "Hel-lo Mr. Hoover."

He looked befuddled, then pulled off his straw hat and mumbled, "Hullo."

As he continued weaving down the street, Margaret looked after him disdainfully. "That Mr. Hoover," she said with a snort of disgust; "my mother says he hasn't drawn a sober breath since his wife died."

She continued to stare at him with intolerance as he stumbled when he came to the cover on the sewer, and I guessed she wasn't as sophisticated about superstitions as she made out, because she seemed to notice for the first time he was wearing a straw hat.

"Straw hat!" she said suddenly, and licked the third finger-tip of her right hand, touched it briefly to her left palm, made a fist with her right hand, then "stamped" her left palm with it, making a resounding thump.

Later on in the afternoon, a fantastic thing happened.

A huge Coca-Cola truck laden with cartons of Coke parked on our street. Then a number of young men of student age leapt down from the truck and proceeded to leave two cartons of Coke at every door, like so many benevolent elves. Within minutes, the street was swarming with kids asking the men if it were really true that they were giving the Coca-Cola away free, and the men laughed and said yes.

Margaret and I looked at each other in amazement. Had everyone at the Coca-Cola Company suddenly gone crazy? They were *giving* it away. Margaret ran home to make sure the cartons had been left at her door, and I went in to get a bottle opener and some magazines. Then we sat on the steps sipping Coke and leafing through them. And when we came to a Coca-Cola ad, we tilted our heads back and drank in the same light-hearted fashion as the people on the page.

Soapy Sobby

That night my aunt's crying again awakened me. Though she was the only divorced person I had ever met; the only lady I knew who smoked; the only lady I knew who stayed blonde through chemistry; and the only person I knew who had been in a branch of "show business," the sound of her crying in the middle of the night dispelled any glamorous image those distinctions might have created. There was nothing glamorous about the sound at all.

I heard my mother get up and go down the hall to her room, then I heard her talk soothingly, then came the sound of water running briefly, and finally the crying became softer but ragged sounding.

To take my mind off it, I plotted another adventure in the life of Soapy Sobby. My fingers fairly itched to be holding a pencil, but I wasn't allowed to get up at night, so I tried my best to imprint in my mind what I'd plotted, in order to write it out the next day.

The next morning, when Margaret phoned to ask what I felt like doing, I told her I was going to be busy, but I didn't tell her what I'd be busy doing. I did tell my mother though. She was always interested in Soapy Sobby, and had seen to it that I had a desk in my room to keep all my writing materials in so I'd have a comfortable place to work, and everything handy when the muse came upon me. Now, my desk was down in the cellar, and everything, it seemed, was in a different place.

"Do you know where there's any paper for me to write on?" I asked her. She thought for a moment. "Perhaps there's some in the living-room desk," she said.

I went into the living room, opened and closed the desk drawers noisily, and rummaged around until I found a scribbler with some blank pages in it.

"Do you know where a pencil is?" I called plaintively from the living room. After some hunting around, my mother finally found one in the kitchen buffet. Then I asked if it would be all right if I wrote at the kitchen table.

"You can for a while dear, but you'll have to move when I start lunch," she said.

With a sigh that I made as audible as possible, I picked up my papers and pencil and went looking for a place to write. The living-room desk wasn't suitable. The flap that pulled down wasn't steady enough. There was a screw missing in one of the hinges, and, in our home, if something was broken it stayed that way. My father and brothers had absolutely no talent for fixing anything. (The doorknob had been off the door of my brothers' room for several years, until one day I borrowed a screwdriver from Nancy's father, and fixed it myself—the whole family was amazed at my mechanical ability!)

I couldn't write out on the front steps, because the other kids would come along and ask what I was doing. The dining-room table had a piece of material on it, with the paper of a dress pattern pinned to it, that my mother was going to cut out that day, so I finally settled at the gate-leg table in the entry

23

hall, making no bones about how inconvenient the arrangement was. But after that brief display of pique, I was soon lost in the world of Soapy Sobby.

I had written my first story about her the year before, the inspiration having come when I was in the bathtub. I had left the soap in the water, and it had gone soft, so when I picked it up I found I could squeeze it into different shapes. The shape I squeezed it into looked something like a doll. With a little manipulation, I made two arms and legs coming from the body, and I started to imagine what it would be like if this doll were a little girl who happened to be made of soap.

When I had gotten dried and dressed, I told my mother I was going to make a book, and she thought I meant I was going to make a booklet, as I'd done before, by folding and cutting paper and binding it with string, but I said I meant to write one this time, so she provided me with paper and pencil and I wrote the first of many adventures in the life of Soapy Sobby.

Soapy Sobby was a little girl who was made of soap, and was always sobbing because none of the other kids would play with her. They just made fun of her, and called her Soapy Sobby, which made her sob all the more, and when she cried bubbles ran down her cheeks.

She had one ambition: to become a real little girl. All her adventures hinged on that desire.

The plot I had worked out the night before, as I tried not to listen to my aunt crying, had Soapy leaving home because no one would play with her. She walked and walked until she came to a little town she'd never seen before, where she stopped to rest in front of a quaint little house, which looked so inviting she walked up the path and knocked on the door.

It was opened by an old lady, who, wonder of wonders, was made of soap too, just like Soapy Sobby. Her name was Mrs. Sudsy, and she was happy to see Soapy because she had believed herself to be the only soap person in the world. She invited Soapy in, gave her supper, read her a story and fixed up a bed for her. That was the first night that Soapy didn't sob herself to sleep.

The next morning she was awakened by a loud crash, and

she jumped out of bed and ran to see what had caused it. When she looked down the basement stairs she saw what had happened. Mrs. Sudsy had fallen down the steps and was lying on the cellar floor all broken up into little pieces.

Soapy bent over the pieces and began to sob. As her tears fell on the soap, bubbles began to form, until there was a pillar of soapsuds the size of a person, and out of this pillar stepped a beautiful fairy.

The fairy told Soapy she had been summoned by Soapy's tears because they were the first Soapy had shed for someone else. Then she told Soapy she could make one wish and it would be granted.

Before Soapy had a chance to say she wanted to be changed into a real little girl, the fairy pointed out that if she should wish that Mrs. Sudsy be put back together again, she would be, but she reminded Soapy she only had one wish.

This threw Soapy into a quandary. On the one hand, she wanted her new-found friend restored to one piece, but, on the other, all her life she had dreamed of becoming a real little girl. She looked sadly at the broken pieces of her new friend, then asked to be transformed into a real little girl. The fairy said first she must promise never to tell anyone how she became real, and Soapy promised. Then the fairy waved her wand, and Soapy became a real little girl.

She was so thrilled that she ran all the way home to show the other kids, and the first thing they asked her was how it had happened. In her excitement she forgot her promise, and told them all about it. When she finished there was a loud clap of thunder, and it began to rain. The other girls just got wet, but a lather began to form on Soapy, and when she saw it she realized she had been changed back into a soap girl, so she began to sob.

When I finished this story, I was pleased with it, and went out to the kitchen with the intention of reading it to my mother, but she told me distractedly that she couldn't listen right then because she was just about to give my aunt a sponge bath. I was stung by her lack of interest. It was the first time she hadn't dropped everything to listen to a Soapy Sobby story, and I went out to sit on the front steps and brood about it.

As I sat there I put to use a large display card I had plucked from the trash in back of a hosiery store on Sherbrooke Street. It was a life-sized cutout of two chiffon-stockinged, fully-developed legs. I sat on the top step with the cardboard cutout resting a step or two below me, with my own skinny legs tucked behind it, and my skirt pulled down over the top of it. After each person had walked past, they'd turn their heads to look again, their eyes riveted to my gorgeous legs.

"Hey, look at the legs on the philosopher!" Walter, a boy who lived down the street, yelled. He always called me that, and though I didn't know what it meant I could tell it was something uncomplimentary by the way he said it. Except for calling back to him, "Takes one to know one," I ignored him, but continued to enjoy the double takes of the other passers-by as I sat waiting for my father to come home.

You forgot to say, "May I?"

That evening, while my mother and sister did the dishes, I went into the living room to have a chat with my father. I always felt a bit shy when I talked to him. He had been fifty when I was born, and our relationship was more like grandfather and grandchild than father and daughter.

Standing in front of his chair, I said, tentatively, "Dad?"

He looked up from his book with that unseeing look people get when they're interrupted while engrossed in something.

"Hello?" he said—not by way of greeting. It was his way of saying, "Yes? What do you want?" or "What can I do for you?" It always made me smile when he said it.

"Can I talk to you a minute?" I asked.

"Of course. What is it, Mary?"

He had one leg up on the footstool in front of him, and he moved it aside so I could sit down. When he was three years old, he had broken that leg in three places from falling off a fence, and the breaks had never mended properly, so he had been lame ever since. He had to have his shoes especially made for him in Toronto, and kept in fine repair by a shoemaker on Sherbrooke Street. The leg still bothered him, and it eased him to have it up on a footstool.

He closed his book with his finger between the pages where he'd left off reading, and looked at me, waiting.

I didn't know what I had in mind exactly when I sought him out for this conversation, other than to try to enlist his aid in getting my aunt to leave, so for openers I asked if he liked having her living with us.

He looked surprised at the question, and, lowering his voice, countered with another: "Do you?"

"No," I said.

His expression didn't change, and he said, "I know it's inconvenient for you—having to sleep in here, and having your aunt take up so much of your mother's time."

"Why did she have to come here anyway?" I asked resentfully. "Why couldn't she've stayed at her brother's? After all, she was there when she got sick, and he has a big house and everything."

"Keep your voice down, dear," he cautioned quietly. "Well, as you know, your aunt is your mother's sister, and there are fewer problems when a sister looks after a sister than when a sister-in-law has to do it."

"Why couldn't she go to a hospital then?"

"For lots of reasons. First of all, she's not sick in the way that calls for hospital care. A Nursing Home or Convalescent Home would be a more suitable place for her to recuperate in than a hospital. But those places cost money, and I can't afford anything like that right now. As it is, there are going to be her doctor's bills and medicine to pay for, and then there's your brother's college tuition fees this fall—anyway, a Nursing Home wouldn't be able to give her the kind of care she requires. She needs someone to bolster her confidence in herself, and help her to believe she can get well. She's been through a lot that you're too young to understand. I know this is hard for you—being displaced this way—but . . .," he spread his hands in a gesture of helplessness.

"But there's no room to do anything around here. My desk's in the basement; I don't have any place to write anymore. . . ."

"That's not true," my father contradicted. "As long as you have your knees and a pencil and paper, you have the wherewithal for writing. Don't fall into the trap of thinking you have to have everything just so before you can write. Many a would-be author has thought that and ended up never writing anything. If you want to be a writer, as you say, then you'd better get into the habit of being able to write anytime, anywhere, under any conditions.

"I knew men at the *Tely* who used to say if only they could get over to Paris they'd be able to write the book they'd been talking about writing for years. And now I know men at the *Star* who say if only they had a little place out in the Townships, or up in the Laurentians or down in Vermont, they'd be able to write a book. That's a lot of hogwash. If they did manage to get such a place, they'd think of another excuse for not writing."

While he was speaking, something occurred to me. When I'd been rummaging around in the basement looking for the paint for the doll houses, I had come across some hard tubes of paint, some of my father's paintbrushes, and his palette and easel, as well as some empty, dusty canvases.

"How come you never paint anymore then?" I asked, figuring I had him.

"Perhaps I've fallen into the trap I just spoke of myself," he admitted. "But you're a little girl; you have your whole life ahead of you, and you're just forming your working habits. So be sure they're good ones. Anyway, you did find some place to write a story today, didn't you?"

I nodded.

"Well then, don't go making out that because your aunt's here you can't write anymore. Besides, a little hardship never hurt any writer."

I must have looked wounded at such callousness because his voice softened when he said, "Do you remember that song you

29

used to sing that went, 'Have you ever been lonely? Have you ever been blue?' "

I nodded again. That had been one of the first songs my sister had taught me, and I had sung it whenever and wherever anyone had requested it.

"Well, you never really have known what it is to be lonely. And maybe just now you're finding out what it's like to be blue. But your aunt has been lonely and blue for a long time." After a pause, he asked curiously, "Don't you feel sorry for her at all?"

"Well yes," I said. "I mean I think it's too bad she's sick and all. . . ."

"Well then, try to put up with the inconvenience as gracefully as possible, and hope it won't be for too long."

I could see I wasn't making an ally in my cause out of him.

I looked up at the massive portrait of Napoleon on the wall over his head. My father had done it when he was only fifteen. Napoleon's brooding look was more compatible to my mood than my father's sympathetic but matter-of-fact expression.

My father had inherited the artistic talents of his grandfather, Robert Clow Todd, one of the earliest Canadian genre painters, who had come to Quebec from Berwick-on-Tweed in 1834, and lived near Montmorency Falls, using them as the subject of many of his canvases. He also used them as background for the many portraits of horses he painted, commissioned by Quebec gentlemen who wanted their favourite bluebloods preserved on canvas.

My father had told me that his grandfather's powers of concentration were so intense while he was painting, that sometimes he would suddenly become aware that a group of Indians had come up silently behind him and had been standing there watching him paint.

Every winter, a huge cone of ice formed at the base of the falls, and my grandfather told my father about the times he and his brothers cut steps into the land side of the cone, and then would slide on their homemade sleds from the top of the cone out onto the ice on the river, as my great-grandfather captured the scene on canvas.

30

Great-grandfather moved to Toronto, however, in 1856, shortly after Cornelius Krieghoff arrived in Quebec, feeling there wasn't room in the province for the two of them.

Because my father was lame, and couldn't take part in sports and other similar activities, he spent his childhood reading and developing his artistic talent. But since we'd moved to Montreal, where he did art work during the day at the *Star*, he had given up painting in the evening and on weekends, and spent most of his spare time reading, sitting in his big chair in the living room with his pipe in his mouth, his leg up on a footstool, a light at his shoulder, his books overcrowding his bookshelves and surrounding tables, and Napoleon brooding above all.

My father did all of his travelling in that chair. He had gone down the Nile with Emil Ludwig, learned about the wild grizzlies of Alaska with John M. Holzworth, and sojourned in Spain with a man called Cervantes. Once he went through a period of being enamoured of Mexico. He read everything he could find about that country, and at the dinner table would describe its vivid colours and bright sunshine, and tell how our family could live there on mere pennies a day. My mother would be able to employ servants, while he earned his living painting.

Somehow I got the idea that we were indeed going to move to Mexico, and prematurely gave out the news at school, being careful to pronounce it May-hee-co, as I'd heard it pronounced on the radio.

I didn't recognize my father's talk for the pipedream it was, nor realize it was his way of coping with the life of "quiet desperation" that the mass of men were leading in the nineteen thirties.

I must have heaved a sigh as I took my eyes away from Napoleon, because my father said, "I'm sorry, dear. But you'll just have to learn to make the best of things you can't change.

That had the ring of a quotation about it, and I wasn't in the mood for quotations just then.

One of his talents was his ability to come up with just the right quote at the proper moment. Sometimes they were so apt that I thought he must make them up. He had a phenomenal memory for passages he liked, and had read and reread Shakespeare's plays so often that he seemed to have an appropriate quote for any occasion.

If I exaggerated, which was my wont, he'd admonish me to "Tell the truth and shame the devil." If my brothers and sisters argued at the dinner table, which was their inclination, he'd remark, "Unquiet meals make ill digestions." If I was unsympathetic, he'd say, "She jests at scars, that never felt a wound." Or if I was jabbering aimlessly on the telephone, he'd say, "She speaks, yet she says nothing." Somehow being chid in the iambic pentameter took the sting out of the rebuke.

His speech was sprinkled with so many literary references that I became acquainted with many characters in literature long before I encountered them in books. When I did come upon them, it was like meeting old friends. I had always known, for instance, that Oliver Twist had asked for more; that Barkis was willin'; and that Marley was dead to begin with.

I could see now he had no more words of solace or suggestions to offer me, so I picked up my book and went over and flopped down on the couch to read. From force of habit, he glanced at the title of my book and *A Girl of the Limberlost* must have met with his approval because he didn't say anything about it, but just opened his book and resumed his reading.

He was such a fast and voracious reader that he had a hard time keeping himself supplied with reading material, borrowing from one or two libraries downtown, and from a lending library near the park on Sherbrooke St. in N.D.G.

He was fussy about what he read himself, and wouldn't tolerate my reading trash either. His objections to bad literature weren't based on moral grounds so much as aesthetic ones, and he indicated his disapproval of a poor choice by subtle, or perhaps not so subtle, ridicule.

If he saw me reading one of the series books like *Bunny Brown and His Sister Sue, Honeybunch, The Bobbsey Twins* or *Nancy Drew*, he'd pick up the book, glance at the title and pretend to read, *Tom Swift and His Electric Grandmother*, or, *Little Willie by the Seashore and Other Tales*—which seemed to sum up for him all that was banal in children's literature. Or he might pick up one of what I considered my "grown-up" books, open it and pretend to read: " 'Oh Lily!' said Violet. 'Oh Violet!' said Lily. 'She dropped her eyes, and he lost his head.' "

My reading tastes ranged from one extreme to another. Before my aunt came to live with us, my mother had always read aloud to me from books she happened to be reading for her own enjoyment—not necessarily the entire book, but, if she were reading and she came across something she thought would or should interest me, she'd say, "Listen to this," then read either a paragraph or a whole chapter. It didn't always interest me. She once tried to read me Stephen Leacock's *My Financial Career*, but laughed so much she never got through it. The only children's books I remember her reading me were *The Real Mother Goose*, which had delightful illustrations; the moralizing tales that Tolstoy wrote for children; and the most exciting and best fairy tale ever written, a book called *Princess Myra*, which my father had won as a boy for perfect Sunday school attendance. Apart from those, she read me her own favourite books. One of these was *Sesame and Lilies*, by John Ruskin. I enjoyed the sense of being bawled out I got when listening to Ruskin's admonitions; there were whole chapters in the book addressed to little girls. And since my mother's favourite writer was Dickens, she read many of his novels, or parts of them, to me.

The winter before, when I had been confined to bed, sick, she had read me a chapter from *Dombey & Son* every day. She had studied elocution, so she acted out every part as she read, but sometimes she'd become so moved by Dickens' imagery and her own eloquence that her voice would begin to wobble, as it did the afternoon she was reading about the death of little Paul Dombey. I had pretended not to notice the change in her voice, then I had to concentrate on pretending I

33

wasn't crying, then I saw a tear slip out of my mother's eye and slowly slide down her cheek, as she read bravely on, and a sob escaped me, which started my mother's tears to really flowing and her voice wobbling all the more, but, laughing at herself shakily through the tears, and dabbing at her eyes, she managed to get through the chapter.

As I had sat on the front steps that afternoon, brooding about my mother not having time to listen to me read my story because of my aunt, I wondered if she would ever have time to read to me again. And what fun would there be in staying home from school sick, now that my aunt was there?

While I enjoyed being read Dickens, I also liked reading the advertisements in the magazines and newspapers that came into the flat. Many of them had plot, conflict, and, ultimately, romance. I particularly liked the Listerine ads. "Even her best friend won't tell her," the caption read, but her best friend, I noticed, would tell everyone else within earshot. And, unfortunately, the poor girl with halitosis would overhear her best friend blabbing it around and ending with, "If only she'd use Listerine!" Then you'd see the girl gargling with Listerine, and then she'd be at a dance, and someone would be cutting in on her partner, and there'd be a whole stag line lined up waiting for the pleasure of dancing with her, the word having gotten around fast that her breath had sweetened up.

My favourite ads of all were the Fleischmann's Yeast ads. I liked them best because they were in comic strip form.

In one series, you'd see a girl with a very bad complexion, looking into a mirror and frowning. Then you'd see her reading a magazine ad for Fleischmann's Yeast. Then you'd see her biting into a yeast cake and smiling. Then, in the final panel, after the legend *Six weeks later*, you'd see her with her skin all cleared up, and she'd be holding the telephone receiver and attached to the other end of the line would be a handsome man, and she'd be saying to him, "Righto, Bob. See you at eight."

Or else you'd see a very skinny girl walking along the beach in a black wool bathing suit. Her chest would be concave, her back spavined, and her arms and legs like pipe cleaners. As she walked along, a group of rowdies would call out to her, "Hey, skinny!" Or she'd be walking with another girl who was all rounded and curved, and the young men would call out callously, "Ethel, who's your skinny friend?"

My heart went out to this poor skinny girl, since I was skinny myself, so I rejoiced when, after the humiliation on the beach, she'd do the sensible thing and start eating Fleischmann's Yeast. And before you knew it her figure had filled out, and all the insensitive louts on the beach would be gathered around her, vying for her attention.

Sometimes I wondered fleetingly why I could readily sympathize with the protagonists in advertisements, soap operas and Victorian novels, but not with my aunt, whose problems couldn't be solved with a bottle of Listerine or a cake of yeast. But I didn't dwell on the thought long; it being too complicated for me.

Perhaps I liked the ads because they were so uncomplicated and easy to understand. I didn't always understand every word in the books I read. For instance, that evening as I lay on the couch reading *A Girl of the Limberlost*, I came to a sentence that stopped me: "He could see the throb of her breast under its thin covering." I didn't know what throb meant, but I didn't want to ask my father. If it turned out to be what I thought it was, I'd be embarrassed.

I also had difficulty in understanding some spoken words: For my first year at school, called "preparatory class," but known to all as "baby class," I had had a teacher who called me by a name I didn't understand, and couldn't pronounce when I got home. It was the way she always addressed me, but I could never quite get my tongue around it.

Then one night at the dinner table, my father used the word in connection with something else, and I pounced on it. "That's what my teacher says I am," I told him triumphantly, "insignificant."

As I read, the street chants outside the open living-room window began to intrude on my consciousness:

One potato,
two potato,

three potato,
four.
Five potato,
six potato,
seven potato,
more.

That meant they were choosing up sides for a game, so I put down *A Girl of the Limberlost* and went out to join them.

The Golden Chariot

As the summer slipped by, and my aunt's condition showed no sign of improvement, we kids continued to read, talk, play street games, and devise new uses for orange crates, peach baskets, shoe boxes and empty spools.

When we tired of the doll houses, we made a grocery store out of them, by standing them against a wall and putting some of our mothers' empty grocery boxes on the shelves. Then we laid another orange crate on its side for a counter, and we were in business. For that venture, in addition to giving us the extra orange crates, our friend Arnold supplied us with order pads with carbon paper between each page, which added a professional touch to the enterprise.

We used the peach baskets to make bassinets for our dolls, by folding the orange mesh covering back over the handle, thumbtacking it to the back of the basket and tacking a skirt around it.

We had lots of peach baskets to work with, left over from the previous autumn. Every fall my mother put up large quantities of jams and jellies, just as many other mothers did. At preserving time, the whole neighbourhood smelled of the bubbling preserves. When you came in from outdoors and were assailed by the delightful fragrance coming from the kitchen, you could hardly wait for the jam or relish to be done so you could have some on bread. We had a pantry off the kitchen with shelves from floor to ceiling, and, as the fruits and vegetables gradually came into season, these shelves began to fill up. I used to gaze at the row upon row of jars of preserves and feel we were prepared for any emergency—be it war, famine or sudden poverty. That had always been a highlight of the fall.

I wondered, as I made a bassinet out of one of the wooden peach baskets, if my mother would have time for preserving this year. If not, that would be one more deprivation because of my aunt's presence in the household, and in a burst of self-pity I added it to my ever-growing grievance list.

When we tired of store-bought paper dolls of people like Deanna Durbin, Jane Withers, Gloria Jean or Shirley Temple, we leafed through fashion magazines, or pattern books we got free from the five and ten, and looked for pictures of models standing in the same pose. Then we made our own paper dolls. We made dollhouses for them, too, by cutting pictures of rooms out of magazines and pasting them around the inside of a shoe box.

Another of our summertime pursuits was called "cork work," although there was no cork involved. What was involved was an empty spool with four nails on top. Onto these nails you put some wool, and then, using another nail, you lifted the wool over the nails, which resulted in a rope of wool that gradually made its way down the centre of the spool.

We took our cork work with us everywhere, even working it while roller-skating, and as the end of the summer drew near our ropes of wool were several feet long.

The ultimate aim of all this work was to get the rope long

enough so that it could be coiled and sewn together to make a rug or mat of some kind, but I never got around to sewing it together, and I didn't know anyone who had.

Another thing we did was send away for things. If there was a blank to be filled in in a periodical, we filled it in. It didn't really matter much what it was for. We received seed catalogues, diets from insurance companies, encyclopedia information, and a Chris Craft catalogue that showed what kind of cabin cruiser we could get for $75,000.

The only things my mother wouldn't let me send away for were things that were advertised as being sent in a plain, unmarked envelope. She said it must mean it was something the postman shouldn't know about, and, if he shouldn't know about it, neither should I.

But I sent Ovaltine tops to Orphan Annie for a ring with my birthstone in it, and Rinso tops to Big Sister for a cameo brooch, and Oxydol tops to Ma Perkins for packages of seeds —all in anticipation of those wonderful words: "The postman brought something for you today."

When all of these forms of entertainment palled, we put together jigsaw puzzles, cut out the Campbell Kids in the Campbell Soup ads in the *Saturday Evening Post*, or resorted to crayoning the cards that came in the shredded wheat boxes.

Or sometimes, when we'd be just sitting on the front steps with nothing else to do, some of the kids would bring me magazines to smell. They would blindfold me first, then someone would hold a magazine to my nose and I would identify it by its smell.

I had first developed this talent when my *Wee Wisdom* magazine came each month, and I'd bury my nose in it as soon as I got it. Then, when my brother started selling *Liberty*, I noticed it, too, had a distinctive smell. Then I went around sniffing the other magazines that came into the flat; *The Saturday Evening Post*, *Collier's*, *Life*, *Time*, the *National Geographic*—all had their own peculiar identifiable smell.

It wasn't a particularly valuable talent to have—you couldn't go on The Major Bowes Amateur Hour with it—but it helped pass the time.

Another way of passing time was to pick scabs off your knees. This was an art not all were proficient in. I happened to be good at it because I got a lot of practice; I generally had one good scab going on at least one knee all summer—often even having scabs on scabs. That was from being overeager to get at them, and starting to pick too soon. What you did, once the scab was hardened, was to lift it ever so gently around the edges, to see if it was white underneath. A faint pinkness was okay too. But if there was the slightest evidence of red, you had to leave it alone till another day.

It was a good way to occupy yourself while you were talking to someone, either in person, or on the phone; or when your friend's mother made you wait outside while they finished eating; or while waiting your turn at a game—although it required such intense concentration you might sometimes miss your turn when it came.

Probably city kids had more scabby knees than other kids because of all the cement, asphalt and macadam around.

Radio also played an important part in filling the hours during summer vacation. You got a chance to hear a lot of daytime shows you missed during school. "Don McNeill's Breakfast Club" from Chicago was one, and then the soap operas: "Dan Harding's Wife," "Peter McGregor," "Big Sister" and "Ma Perkins," to name but a few.

My mother listened to these programs as she sat in the dining room at the sewing machine making clothes for us. (My aunt listened to them in her room on her own Gothic table model radio.) As my mother changed bobbins, cut out patterns, basted and put the finishing touches to her handiwork, somehow she managed to keep track of the fortunes of all the different characters.

The two serials I liked the best were "Ma Perkins" and "Big Sister," which came on at 11:15 a.m. and 11:30 a.m. respectively. Ma owned a lumberyard in Rushville Centre. Her sidekick was Shuffle Shober, which she pronounced "Sheffle," and she had two daughters who were as different as night and day. One was named Evey, and was married to Willy Fitz, and the other was Fay, who had one piece of hard luck after another.

Big Sister had a brother named Neddy—I can't remember if she had a sister too—and was married to Dr. John Wayne, played by Martin Gabel. I used to tingle when I heard that mellow voice, which sounded as if he'd been sucking McIntosh Toffee.

The best family serial of all was "One Man's Family," which was "dedicated to the mothers and fathers of the younger generation, and their bewildering offspring."

Father and Mother Barbour's own bewildering offspring were Paul, Hazel (who always addressed her father as "Father Barbour"), the twins, Clifford and Claudia, and Jack. Paul, who was unmarried, for some reason had a daughter named Teddy, who was his ward or adopted daughter or something. The locale of the story was San Francisco, and whenever Teddy wanted to think things out she went down to sit on the "sea wall" and stare at the ocean. How I envied her that sea wall.

Sometimes Father Barbour would become so bewildered by the lot of them, he'd sigh, and say to Mother Barbour, "Oh, Fanny, Fanny, Fanny, Fanny, Fanny, Fanny."

Another show we got a kick out of was "Vic and Sade," "Radio's home folks," who lived "in the little house half way down the next block" and had a cast of characters with fascinating names. Vic and Sade Gook's son's name was Rush, and Vic called him Dishrag. Rush's two best friends were Smelly Clark and Blue Tooth Johnson, and two of the men who dropped by regularly were the Brick Mush Man, who was always crying, and Mr. Gump Box, with his horse, Howard.

Vic belonged to a fraternal organization called The Sacred Stars of The Milky Way—R. J. Kunk was its beloved founder. A picture of him hung on the wall where they held their monthly meetings, "down to the Bright Kentucky Hotel." The picture had eyes that not only lit up, but they followed you around the room. Other members were Y. Y. Flirtch, Uncle Fletcher, Y. Y. I. Y. Skeber, Alf Musherton and Richigan Fishigan from Sishigan, Michigan.

Our laughter at such programmes, since the advent of an invalid to the household, became muted, almost furtive, seldom erupting spontaneously and loudly as it had before.

Every now and then, the sameness of the summer days was interrupted by something interesting. For example, a car radiator might get overheated and a stream of boiling water and steam would gush up from it, and we would all stand around watching gleefully until someone took the driver a kettle of water to cool it off.

Or the scissors- and knife-sharpener man would come down the street, park his grindstone on its wooden treadle against the curb, and ring a bell so all the people on the street would know he was there. We liked to watch him and hear the shivery sounds the knife made when he held it against the grindstone.

Or you could watch the man who came around once a week to cut the grass. After he'd finished mowing, he'd sweep the grass cuttings away, leaving a beautifully neat lawn behind him. For this service he charged fifteen cents.

Or the old man, whose creased face was crisscrossed with a network of fine lines, would drive his wagon by and call out, "Rags, bones, and bottles." We never knew whether he was buying or selling them.

Another man who came around regularly was the egg man, who carried a basket of eggs piled one on top of the other, with only a little bit of straw between the layers, and went from door to door selling them. My father once remarked that a jostle on the streetcar would wipe out his inventory, but the egg man didn't seem to worry about that prospect. We kids liked him because he didn't ignore us as many adults did. He told me once that his son was the image of Eddie Cantor, and had gone to Hollywood to try to get a job as his stand-in.

Yet another man, who dropped by periodically to collect premiums, was Mr. Carmichael, the insurance man. Jack Benny at that time had a running gag on his programme involving a polar bear named Carmichael that lived in his basement and had eaten the gas man when he came to read the metre, so when the insurance man came, my mother and I could hardly keep our faces straight when we called him by name.

Sometimes the water truck would come down the street, sluicing the horse manure, popsicle sticks, gum wrappers and other gutter accumulation into the sewers.

Another day, the sewer cleaners came to perform their messy, smelly work, and we watched as they brought up some familiar objects in their gigantic ladles. Margaret saw the lacrosse ball she'd lost the previous spring, but she wouldn't touch it; it was so slimy. And I recognized the toque that Walter, the boy down the street, had snatched from my head and stuffed down the sewer the winter before.

Cement mixing was always well worth a few minutes watching time too. The men who repaired the city sidewalks had long troughs, into which they poured bags of cement and pails of water. Then, with a long hoe, they stirred the mushy mixture, pushing it back and forth and around the trough. It looked like the greatest, muckiest kind of job to have. But the men's expressions as they worked indicated that they didn't realize how much fun their job was.

(Nor, for that matter, did the coal men, who came around in the late fall and winter, delivering coal. They'd back the coal truck up to the coalbin window of your basement, one man calling the signals to the driver, "Bagup. Bagup." Then they'd slant a metal chute between the truck and the window, and dump burlap bags full of coal down the chute, making a racket you had to cover your ears against. But as they rubbed a blackened hand across a brow already black with coal dust, they didn't look as if they were enjoying themselves, which was curious, considering that any small boy watching would've given his eyeteeth to be doing the same job—without pay.)

One day that summer we had some real excitement. Margaret and I were walking down by the railroad tracks, that bisected N.D.G., when we spotted a two dollar bill lying on the other side of the steel fence between us and the tracks. Margaret reached under the fence and retrieved it, and we ran home to show it to her mother, who clasped her hands together when she saw it, and looked as if she didn't know whether to scream or go blind. Margaret's father was a ship's purser, and was seldom home, and it looked as if that two dollars was the answer to a prayer because Margaret's mother immediately wrote out a shopping list of groceries she needed, and we took it and the two dollars up to the grocery store.

Two dollars bought a lot of groceries.

You could get ten pounds of new potatoes for nine cents. Boneless pot roast was fifteen cents a pound. A rolled rib roast was twenty-nine cents a pound. Bread was ten cents a loaf, and milk ten cents a quart. Two dozen ears of corn cost twenty-seven cents. A pound of tea was fifty-four cents, and a pound of coffee twenty-nine. You could take home two pounds of bacon for forty-five cents, and ten pounds of sugar for fifty-three.

Bubbling with excitement, we told Arnold, who was pretending to be a French Canadian that day, how we found the money. He listened gravely to the story and then said, "Dose two dollar, you found dat where?"

"Somewhere between Harvard and Marcil, I think."

"Ahahnh. It's very strange, dat."

"What is?"

"Yesterday, h'om walking along dere between 'Arvard and Marcil, and h'om lose two dollar."

"Oh Arnold, you're just saying that," Margaret protested.

"Would Harnold tell a lie? H'om walk along by the railroad track. In my 'and is a two dollar, and poof! The wind she come and blow h'it away."

"Oh Arnold, that's not true," Margaret said.

"Never mind. Dose two dollar, it are probably not the same."

"Did you really lose two dollars. Honestly?" Margaret persisted.

"*Mais oui.* But don' worry 'bout dat. Just tell me what your mother want."

"Oh Arnold, say you didn't really lose two dollars," Margaret pleaded. But Arnold kept changing the subject, and when we left we were still uncertain as to whether he was teasing or not.

All that summer, as in summers past, there were men who were down on their luck coming to the door and asking for something to eat. My mother often prepared food for them and served it to them on the front steps. Sometimes I'd sit on the steps and talk to them as they wolfed down their meal.

Some of the men who came around were scarcely more than boys, and the main thing on their minds was food—the food they were eating at the moment, and the food they hoped to be eating in the near future. One such youth told me he was a graduate of a university in California, but, since he couldn't find a job there, he had come to Canada hoping to find work. He told me about the relief stations and missions he'd eaten at while travelling across the country, and he said he couldn't remember the last time he'd eaten meat. His clothes hung on his gaunt frame, and when he told me that I was sorry the sandwich my mother had made for him was a fried egg one.

Sometimes my mother made sandwiches for the transients to take with them. One time a man came to the door and said he was hungry, so my mother made up a batch of sandwiches for him and put them in a bag. Then I saw the man drop the unopened bag into one of the trash barrels outside the back door of the grocery store at the corner.

I came bursting into the house, spluttering with indignation after witnessing this, and was all set to tell my mother about it. But she was on the phone having one of her lengthy conversations with Mrs. Teasdale, a next door neighbour, and, since I had to tell somebody, I stopped in my aunt's doorway and told her. She shook her head ruefully when I had finished.

"Why would he *do* a thing like that?" I demanded.

"I don't know. I suppose what he really wanted was money —perhaps to buy a drink, and he wasn't interested in food."

"Boy, is Mom ever going to be mad when I tell her."

45

"Why tell her?"

"What do you mean? Why wouldn't I tell her?"

"She's probably feeling good because she thinks the man is enjoying a meal because of her. So why spoil her good feeling by telling her that her kindness wasn't appreciated?"

"Well, I. . . . I mean, gee whiz. . . . Well, yes, I see what you mean." I finally agreed, and went outside again without waiting to speak to my mother.

One time the doorbell rang in the evening, and I opened the door to a man who asked to see my father. He was a newspaperman who had been laid off, and he said he was on his way to Toronto. He didn't have the train fare, so was walking, and perhaps going to ride a freight. My father had a courtly, almost old-world manner with people who came to our home, and, though he knew the man only slightly, he brought him in and called my mother to bring a snack. As the man ate, my father wrote out the names of the people for him to see at *The Telegram*, the *Star*, and *The Globe and Mail* in Toronto. Then my mother packed him a lunch and the man rose to go.

As he was leaving, I saw my father slip some money into his hand as he wished him good luck, and, as the man gratefully pocketed the money, I got the same feeling I got when my mother told me the story of the old shoemaker who had the idea that God was going to visit him one day, but the only people who came were a ragged boy, an old street sweeper and a woman with a sick baby. So while the old man waited for God's visit, he did all he could to make these unfortunates comfortable. And, at the end of the day, when the disappointed shoemaker read in his Bible the words: "I was hungry and ye gave me meat. I was a stranger and ye took me in. Verily I say unto you, inasmuch as ye have done it unto the least of my brethren, ye have done it unto me," he realized that God had come to visit him in the persons of the street sweeper, the urchin and the mother.

As my father went back into the living room and picked up his book after the man had gone, I wondered if he realized Who had just left. When I asked him, he looked up and said,

"Yes. There, but for the grace of God, go I."

Another person who came to the door at least once every season was Mr. Popov, the old-clothes man, who drove a late-model car, and carried a fat roll of bills in his back pocket, kept intact with a rubber band.

That summer when he came by, as usual, my mother hunted up some old clothes and I hung around to listen to their conversation.

"Wot have you got to sell?" he began the interview warily.

"Well," my mother said, smiling like a carnival pitchman, "I have my son's lovely warm winter overcoat; this practically brand new suit (my husband will have a fit when he finds out I've sold it) and these grand rubber wading boots."

Mr. Popov picked up the waders disdainfully and dropped them in an out-of-the-way corner. "Nobody's interested in those things," he said in his strong Russian accent.

My mother felt called upon to defend the boots. "They're perfectly good," she said indignantly. "They've only been worn a few times. My son bought them for fishing—and he doesn't like fishing."

But Mr. Popov wasn't listening to her. He was looking over the coat and suit suspiciously, searching for worn spots, frayed cuffs and so on. Giving the impression that he'd satisfied himself that the garments were next to worthless, he shoved them aside and asked, "Have you anything else to sell?"

My mother looked around distractedly, and, when her eye fell on me, I took an involuntary step backward. Shaking her head, she said, "No. Those are the things I have to sell. Take them or leave them."

Mr. Popov felt the coat material and sneered, "You expect that to keep somebody warm?"

"I certainly do," my mother told him. "It's kept my son warm for the past three years."

"Three years? It looks more like ten to me. All the warmth has been worn out of it. I'll take the coat and suit off your hands for two dollars."

At that, my mother gathered up the suit and coat and said,

"There's no point in selling them for that. My son can get lots more good wear out of these things."

Mr. Popov spread his hands and shrugged, "I'm no businessman," he confessed. "I'll give you three dollars for the suit and coat."

"I'll throw in the wading boots," my mother said, "and take four."

Silently, he took the thick wad of bills out of his pocket, and, with a resigned sigh to indicate he was no match for my mother, snapped off the elastic band and counted off four ones.

Then he did what he'd done before at the close of these transactions. They always held their bargaining sessions in the entry hall where the gate-leg table stood, and each time, as he was leaving, after having ignored the table all the while he was there, he would say with studied casualness, "I'll give you a hundred dollars for that table." And my mother would always say, "No." And, from the emphatic way she said it, he could tell she'd brook no arguments about it.

That day, after she had once again declined his offer for the table, saying firmly, "It's not for sale," and he had left, I said, "Gee why don't you sell him that table, Ma? It's all old and everything anyway." And she said, "That was the first piece of furniture your Grandma and Grandpa Choate got when they were married, and they passed it on to your father and me when we were married, and, who knows, we may pass it on to you when you get married. I'll never sell it."

"But gee whiz," I said, "a whole hundred dollars!"

"Oh what's a hundred dollars?" she scoffed. So saying, she slipped the four dollars she had received into her apron pocket then looked momentarily chagrined. "Did you notice that smug look on his face as he was leaving?" she asked me. "I bet I could've held out for five dollars easily."

The cast kept changing in our street games and at our front-step conversation sessions. As one girl went away for her vacation, she was replaced by someone who had just returned.

Luckily, our family had been away for our vacation before my aunt arrived. We had gone to our usual vacation spot, Old

Orchard Beach in Maine. I loved the ocean, beach, pier and amusement area there, and especially the idea that my favourite comedian, Fred Allen, spent his summers there. I kept thinking that any moment I might turn a corner and bump into the baggy-eyed, nasal-voiced humorist, but I never did.

The curious thing about Old Orchard Beach was that when you were there, you were always bumping into people on the street that you bumped into in N.D.G. When you went to church in Old Orchard, all the same people milled about outside after Mass as milled around the church in N.D.G., and, what was even more curious, if you did see someone from N.D.G. in Old Orchard you'd be terrifically happy to see them. Even though when you saw them in N.D.G. you didn't get excited at all. My father had an expression to explain this phenomenon. When I drew it to his attention, he said, "You'd speak to a yellow dog in Kentucky."

The summer didn't go by without drama though. One day, Barbara, one of the girls on the street, failed to join us on the front steps. Then we saw an ambulance stop in front of her flat, and then we heard that Barbara's mother had been taken to the Homeopathic Hospital.

For the next few days, Barbara and Margaret and I walked to Marlowe Avenue where the hospital was, and stood outside looking up at Barbara's mother's window. One day, as we stood looking up at the window, at which Barbara's mother never appeared, Barbara said, "I don't think I'll ever see my mother again." I went cold at the finality of the words as they hung in the air, and was at a loss for a reply. Could there be anything worse than having your mother die? I did not think that there could. I had known only one child whose mother had died—she was in my class at school—her name was Patricia and I used to watch her often when I knew she wasn't aware of being observed. She was the neatest, tidiest girl in our class. The collars and cuffs of her uniform were always freshly laundered. Her nails were always clean, she looked as if she had a bath every night, and she always had her homework done. Her father paid a housekeeper to see to all those things.

The reason I watched her was to see if she looked sad, and what I found curious was that she didn't. She just looked ordinary. She may have been a bit more subdued than the other girls, but then it could have been her nature to be. I never got to know her, so didn't know what her homelife was like, but I could only imagine it as being inexpressibly sad.

Barbara had been right about her mother, and after the funeral she and her brother were sent to live with their grandmother in Fort Covington, New York.

Around the same time, one late afternoon that summer, as we ranged lazily on the front steps, the sickening sound of squealing tires broke the stillness, and we looked down the street to see what had happened. We could see the figure of a boy lying on the road, so we jumped up and ran toward him.

It was Walter, the winter toque-snatcher. He was lying perfectly still, and his eyes were closed. Within moments, Walter's mother was pushing her way through the crowd that had quickly gathered. She knelt down beside him and held on to him saying over and over, "It didn't happen. It didn't happen."

Finally someone thought to phone the Homeopathic Hospital, and then the ambulance took him away.

For several days, Walter hovered between life and death. On Sunday, the priest asked the congregation to pray that he'd "pass the crisis," so, even though he had taken my toque, and I didn't know what a crisis was, I knelt down with the rest of the congregation and said a prayer.

I heard that Walter's mother had made a bargain with God in her prayers that if Walter's life was spared, she would go to Mass and Communion every morning for the rest of her life. Then one day the word was spread that Walter had passed the crisis, and his mother kept her promise, and every morning thereafter could be seen walking up the street on her way to Mass, rain or shine, sleet or hail. On particularly inclement days, I used to wonder if sometimes she wished she hadn't made such an extravagant deal.

Another death on our street that summer, in addition to Barbara's mother, was that of the old lady who lived next door to us who had eighteen cats. Her flat used to reek of cat odour, and she would talk to them as if they were human. If they happened to be lying in every available chair, when you went to visit her, you had to stand, because she'd never ask the cats to move. I seldom went to see her; the smell of the cats was so overpowering.

(She, and another old lady down the street who had a Pekingese, were the only people I knew who had pets.

The only living things that had ever been in *my* charge were two goldfish and a geranium—all of which died for lack of water.)

After the old lady died, her married son unsentimentally gave all her household effects to the Salvation Army, and all the cats to the S.P.C.A., and the landlord painted the flat throughout—walls, ceiling, he even scraped the floors—in an effort to get rid of the cat odour.

Shortly after the decorating was finished, a family moved in that had a daughter around my age. The day after they arrived, the girl came out and sat on a chair on her front porch. She didn't seem to have anything to do, and, since neither had I at the moment, I decided to go over and get acquainted.

Walking up the path, I said, "Hi."

"*Bonjour*," she said.

I was taken aback, because I hadn't known she was French, but I recovered quickly and said, "*Bonjour*."

Her face lit up at my greeting, possibly because she thought she'd have someone to talk to.

"*Comment ça va?*" I asked.

"*Très bien merci*," she said, "*Et vous?*"

"*Pas mal*." I shrugged as Gallically as I could make it, then sat down on the top step. She didn't know it, but she had just heard the extent of my French vocabulary, with the exception of a few isolated words and phrases.

Pointing to myself, I told her my name.

"*Je m'appelle Louise*," she said.

"*Allo, Louise,*" I said, and we both giggled.

She sat winding and unwinding a red yo-yo as I searched my brain for another French phrase. She looked as if she were trying to think of something to say too.

I looked all around, everywhere but at her, and she kept staring at the yo-yo in her hand. Then she looked up just as I was looking at her, and we both smiled.

I put out my hand to borrow her yo-yo, and she gave it to me. I stood up with it and started to show off. I looped the loop, walked the dog, rocked the baby, went around the world, snapped the yo-yo up and out and away from me and flicked it back and forth over my wrist. She looked impressed. After I gave it back to her, there didn't seem to be anything else to do, so I said, "I guess I'll go now." And as I walked down the path, I turned to say, "*Au revoir.*"

From then on we always said "*Bonjour*" to one another as we passed on the street, but we didn't stop to talk.

The most dramatic incident of that summer, however, concerned our friend Arnold.

The back of the grocery store he managed faced on our street, and one morning, early, just after the store opened, a police car drew up to the back door. We kids saw the car there and thought the store might have been robbed. But after a time a long black vehicle drew up to the back door and a figure was carried out on a stretcher, placed in the wagon and driven away, while the store employees stood around with ashen faces. I looked around for Arnold so I could ask him what had happened, but he was nowhere in sight.

Upon the arrival of the long black wagon, a crowd had gathered, and, after it had driven away, before dispersing, everyone was speculating as to what might have happened. Someone had died, they said, that was for sure, because the vehicle hadn't been an ambulance, but who?

I wished Arnold was around. He would have told us. Maybe in a bad Charlie Chan accent, but he would have told us. The next thing we knew, however, the grocery store closed for the day, and the rest of the employees went home. I didn't see Arnold the whole time.

In the afternoon, Mrs. Teasdale phoned. I called my mother to the phone, and she came up the hall drying her hands. She took the receiver from me, said hello, and then simply listened, drawing up a dining-room chair at one point to sit down. As Mrs. Teasdale talked, my mother made clucking sounds, interspersed with the words, "The poor fellow. Oh the poor chap."

I couldn't wait for her to get off the phone so I could ask what had happened. When I asked, however, she looked as if she weren't going to tell me. Then she drew me to her and said, "Arnold was a friend of yours, wasn't he?"

I nodded.

"Well, I hate to have to tell you this dear, but the person they took away today was Arnold."

"You mean Arnold's *dead*?" I asked, incredulous.

"I'm afraid so, Mary."

I started to cry. "How did he die?" I asked.

"Well, Mrs. Teasdale said that Arnold was very much in debt and—you know he had a wife and four children?"

I nodded again. They went to our church, and every Sunday morning the whole family sat in one pew, the four little girls all looking alike, and all just like Arnold, with straight black hair and shiny brown buttons for eyes.

"Well he apparently had a hard time making ends meet, so he started to gamble. Then he went even more into debt, and I guess he began to get sick. . . ."

"Can you get sick from being in debt?"

"Well yes, in a way you can. A person can become mentally sick and despondent. So much so that he does things he wouldn't do if he were well."

"And did Arnold die from being in debt?"

"Well, yes, I guess you could say that," my mother said.

That afternoon, Margaret and I discussed it.

"I wonder if that really *was* his two dollars," Margaret said.

"Oh, I don't think so," I said, although I had misgivings too. "You know how he was always teasing us."

"If it was, it might have helped him with his debt," she said.

Later in the day we heard some of the older boys on the street discussing the incident excitedly.

"They say the delivery boy came in and found him in the basement."

"Boy, *that* would give you the spooks."

"I'd never work *there* again."

"My mom said she'd never buy groceries there again."

"That's stupid."

"Well you know what a nervous Nelly she is."

"How'd he do it anyway?"

"Rope."

"Stood on some packing cases then kicked them over."

"Did he leave a note?"

"I don't know."

One of the boys noticed Margaret and me listening.

"Hey, Big-ears, what're you hanging around for? Gwan home and tell your mother she wants ya."

"Ya. Put an egg in your shoe and beat it."

The next day I overheard my mother and aunt talking about the funeral. My mother said Mrs. Teasdale had told her that Arnold's wife was having a hard time making funeral arrangements. He wasn't allowed to be buried in the Catholic cemetery, even though he had been a Catholic, because suicides are automatically excommunicated. They couldn't have the funeral service at our church either.

I was getting washed in the bathroom which was next door to my aunt's room, and, with the door slightly open, I could hear them clearly.

"I can't understand it," my mother said, and I knew she was shaking her head in bewilderment. "I just can't imagine anyone feeling so low that they could actually take their own life!"

"I can imagine it," I heard my aunt say quietly.

The following Sunday, Arnold's wife and four little girls were occupying their usual pew. The little girls' brown button eyes lacked the lustre they formerly had. When we knelt down to pray for the repose of the souls of the faithful who had departed during the previous week, Arnold's name never came up. It was as though he had never existed—except for the four little girls who kept looking down at their white-gloved hands folded in their laps, as the names were being read out.

During the canon of the Mass, however, when it was time to pray silently for the dead, I mentioned his name, and I guess they did too.

While these events were taking place on our street, there was much going on in the rest of the world. Many cases of infantile paralysis were being reported in Montreal and Toronto. In fact, it was decided there would be no baby show on Labour Day at the Canadian National Exhibition because of the epidemic in Ontario.

Montreal was in the clutch of a heat wave that proved to be the longest on record. It had started at the beginning of July and there was to be no let-up throughout the rest of July and August.

As I walked past my aunt's open door on this succession of hot days, I would sometimes see her sitting by the window, waiting for a breeze to stir the hot, muggy air, but none came.

The Montreal Star, which my father brought home every night damp off the press, said that astrologers were blaming the extreme heat and humidity on the fact that the earth was under the influence of Sirius, the dog star, and that was why we were experiencing these hot, sticky, dog days.

In addition to carrying stories about the heat, the *Star* also reported that the Dionne quintuplets had colds, and that Freddie Bartholomew was feuding with Bobby Breen. Msgr. Camille Roy, rector of Laval University, said that the Separatist Movement was "sheer folly," and that Separatism would mean that French Canadians would have abandoned the vast field of enterprise which is open to them in Canada. The Botanical Gardens were nearing completion. "The Prince and The Pauper" with the Mauch Twins was playing at the Westmount Theatre, and Shirley Temple and Victor McLaughlin were downtown at the Capitol in "Wee Willie Winkie," with a special children's show every day except Sunday for twenty-five cents. Showing on the same bill was the first complete film of the Coronation Procession in "natural colour." Maurice Duplessis, the Premier of Quebec, had given special permission for children to be allowed to see the Coronation film, because the law was that you had to be sixteen to get into a movie theatre in Quebec. The law had originated in 1927, when film was highly flammable and there had been a disastrous fire in a Montreal theatre called the Laurier Palace, in which seventy-seven small children had been burned to death.

Some of the other movies advertised in the newspaper that were playing downtown were: Jean Arthur and Edward Arnold in "Easy Living"; Clarke Gable and Jean Harlow in "Sabotage"; Don Ameche and Ann Sothern in "Fifty Roads to Town"; "The Good Earth" with Paul Muni and Louise Rainer at the Palace; "Seventh Heaven" with Simone Simon and James Stewart at the Imperial; and "Angel's Holiday" with Jane Withers.

In the newspaper ads, the quints were endorsing Colgate dental cream and Palmolive soap, Shirley Temple was endorsing Quaker Puffed Wheat, Burns and Allen endorsed Grape Nuts, and Professor Kindly persuaded mothers to give their babies Castoria. "Babies cry for it." And folks who were looking for Joe were told he had gone for a Dow.

In former years, by the time the summer was this far advanced, our family would have had several visitors from Toronto or the States staying with us at different times. But with my aunt living with us there was no room to entertain overnight guests.

I missed having the visitors because taking them around Montreal afforded me the opportunity of seeing the city myself. I had enjoyed going along with my mother and showing our guests the attractions our city had to offer, such as The Sun Life Building, which was the largest office building in the Commonwealth; and La Fontaine Park, with its coloured fountains; and the magnificent view of the city from the lookouts on top of Mount Royal and Westmount Mountain. Where we took them depended on the visitors' particular interests. If they were of a religious bent, we went to see some of the picturesque and historic churches in which Montreal abounds, such as St. Joseph's Oratory, St. James' Cathedral and Christ Church Cathedral. Or we would go down to Old Montreal and see Nôtre Dame Church and Nôtre Dame de Bonsecours, known as "the sailors' church," with its models of ships hanging from the ceiling that were made by sailors in thanksgiving for reaching port safely. Then, being so handy to it, we would go to Bonsecours Market. If it happened to be on a Tuesday or Friday, we would see the farmers who had driven in to Montreal from miles around with wagons full of vegetables, fruits and flowers. And, in the building itself, the farmers' wives spread out their homespuns, quilts and needlework for sale. Another attraction in Montreal's Old Town was the Château de Ramezay Museum, across from the Court House and City Hall.

If our visitors brought their children with them, sometimes we would go to either Belmont or Dominion amusement parks. And if my cousin, who was a schoolteacher in Toronto, came to visit, we'd go to places like the Indian Reservation of Caughnawaga, or the Montreal Museum of Fine Arts.

The city had so many riches to offer that my heartbeat quickened as I walked or rode amongst its splendours. Looking at the lighted cross on top of the mountain that dominated the city, I couldn't help thinking that surely there couldn't be another city anywhere to match its beauty.

My greatest pleasure was to show off the city from one of Montreal's golden sightseeing streetcars. These cars were baroque affairs, roofless, with tiered seats, and curlicued railings in intricate shapes in a dazzling bright gold colour. Because we had no visitors to take around on it that summer, my mother said she would treat Margaret and me to a ride on the Golden Chariot by ourselves.

The day we chose to go was the day before I'd be returning to school. For some reason, the Catholic schools were reopening on a Thursday, September 2nd, while the heat wave was still on and we were still in the throes of the infantile paralysis epidemic. The Protestant schools, however, weren't opening till the Tuesday after Labour Day, September 7th, and there was even talk of them not opening until October 1st, because of the epidemic.

On our way over to the corner of Girouard and Sherbrooke where we were going to board the golden streetcar, Margaret and I stopped at Heller's for a double-header ice-cream cone. Then, after paying our twenty-five-cent fare, and getting settled, we made our ice creams last as long as possible as the car travelled up Girouard to Snowdon, then east of Snowdon along Queen Mary Road. From this point we could see the Oratory, then, on past The Shrine and the University of Montreal, we went to Outremont.

I had made the trip so often I could almost qualify for tourist guide status, barking out locations of interest and telling their historical significance from my own point of view. As the golden coach turned south at Park Avenue, for instance, going past Fletcher's Field on the right, ignoring the monument of Sir Georges Etienne Cartier which stood in Fletcher's Field, I pointed out to Margaret the small hospital on the left where I'd had my tonsils out.

When we got down to St. Catherine St., we caught sight of my two favourite signs: the big black horse on the Black Horse Brewery, and the big steer on the Bovril sign with the neon tears dripping from its eye and the flashing slogan, "Alas, my poor brother." For a long time I thought Bovril was made from the tears of a steer.

Our golden streetcar travelled west to Atwater, where it turned North to Sherbrooke St., passing the Mother House of the Congregation of Nôtre Dame, and proceeding west into Westmount, where everybody on the car craned their necks to see the clock in Westmount Park which was made of flowers and told the correct time.

We continued on back into our home territory, and jumped down from the car at Girouard and Sherbrooke, our faces pink from the sun beating down on us, and our stomachs queasy from the ice-cream cones combined with the smell of the fumes and the motion of the car.

As I was walking up the path in front of our flat, after saying good-bye to Margaret, I ran back to tap her arm and say, "Last touch." I knew we wouldn't be seeing as much of each other once we started back to school.

Bending the twig

The next morning, all the Catholic kids poured out of their homes like rabbits out of their warrens, and headed for their respective schools.

On the way, I called on Doreen, who had spent the summer at her aunt's in Mooers, New York. I was glad to see her again.

She had always been the smartest girl in the class; one of those people who did everything well. She could knit Argyle socks. She was the best smokie player, the best miniature golfer and the best Monopoly player. The summer before, we had sat on her front steps buying, selling and trading properties to a fare-thee-well. I dropped over a million dollars that summer. Doreen was a Boardwalk and Park Place type of person, while I was strictly Baltic and Marvin Gardens.

The year before in school, after having been painstakingly taught to write in the accepted forward-flowing convent script, she and I spent many an hour perfecting writing backhand, and wrote that way from then on. Nor were Doreen and I satisfied with our given names. For a while we insisted on being called Lola and Priscilla, after the Lane Sisters, stars of "Three Smart Girls". Doreen was an innovator too. She showed us how to make clown dolls out of wool, which we wore as lapel ornaments, and she was responsible for single-handedly originating a hair style that almost everyone in our school took up. Most of us wore our hair straight, with bangs, and one day she devised the idea of braiding the hair on either side of her face and clamping the ends of the braids with barrettes. It looked as if she were wearing a paintbrush in front of each ear, but the style caught on, and soon almost all the girls in the school were wearing their hair that way. She was also one of the three people I knew whose father had a car.

That morning, we got caught up on each other's summer news as we walked to school. I told her about my aunt coming to live with us, and she listened attentively to my recital, then commented, "If only you could find out where her son and husband live."

"What good would that do?"

"Then you could write them and tell them she's sick, then I bet they'd want her to come and live with them."

By that time we had reached the schoolyard, where we renewed acquaintances with girls we hadn't seen since the end of June.

When the bell rang, Doreen and I split up, because for the first time we were going to be in different classes. She was continuing in the A class, and I was going into the B class, so I went to take my place in line with a group of strangers, next to the line of girls who had been in my class since I'd started school. As I stood waiting for our new teacher, I looked over at the familiar faces in the line next to me.

Marie, who was so clean that her skin seemed to be cracked from too much washing, waggled her fingers at me in greeting. Her scribblers were always the neatest and cleanest in the class, and her writing the nicest.

Next to her, looking wan as usual, stood Helen, who usually fainted in church on the first Friday of every month when we went over for Benediction after school. She was extremely pale and blonde, with tiny blue veins visible under her eyes, and when she sat in the sun you could see a whitish blonde fuzz along her cheekbone. Because she was so blonde, she was always chosen to play the part of the Blessed Virgin in school Christmas pageants, and to present flowers to the pastor on his Feast day.

A girl named Betty was standing behind them. She was exceptionally bright and quiet, and never did anything wrong in school. One day, the year before, when she had been standing patiently lined up in ranks in the school hall, just as she was now, the Mother Superior went up to her and slapped her face hard, leaving a bright red mark on Betty's cheek. Betty took a step back in amazement, and didn't even cry out, she was so stunned. All of the other girls were as shocked as she to see poor Betty get slapped that way. Later in the day, the Mother Superior apologized to Betty. She had meant to slap a girl named Millicent, whose hair was cut the same way as Betty's, and she'd mistaken one girl for the other.

Pat, the girl standing beside Betty now, had gotten the strap one day for putting ink in her inkwell.

Standing behind Pat was a German girl named Elsie, whose father was a chauffeur. I often saw him standing in the school corridors in his chauffeur's livery and puttees, holding his cap in his hands and arguing with one of Elsie's teachers. I envied Elsie having a father who would stand up to a nun that way.

I was going to miss the kids in the other class.

After an eternity of waiting, our teacher appeared and led us up to our classroom. She assigned us our desks, and then we sat facing each other, sizing each other up. After taking our names, the names of our parents, our addresses, phone numbers and fathers' occupations, she told us how much money to bring in for our school books and dismissed us.

The next day was a regular school day. We began it with prayers, followed by a Catechism period. Then we wrote a composition on How I Spent My Summer Vacation, being sure

61

to write, at the left-hand top corner of each page in our scribblers, the letters J.M.J. with a tiny cross over the M., to signify that the work we did was for the holy family—Jesus, Mary and Joseph. Before breaking for recess we said a prayer, and before resuming our work we said another one. When the bell rang at noon we said the Angelus before being dismissed for lunch. Before starting our afternoon session, we said a decade of the Rosary and three Glory Be's. We prayed again before and after afternoon recess, and before going home at the end of the school day.

There was about an equal number of lay teachers and nuns in the school. The nuns had to be addressed as Mother. My own mother said that in Toronto they were called Sister, and she could never remember to call my teachers anything else. The nuns were treated with great courtesy by us girls. If you passed one in the hall, you had to step to one side against the nearest wall and bow your head, the way you had to bow your head every time you said or heard the name Jesus.

The school was right across from the church, and we were encouraged to spend as much time there as possible, so before going home that afternoon, Doreen and I dropped into the church to make a visit and say The Stations of the Cross.

As we left the church, Doreen said casually, "I offered up The Stations of the Cross for your aunt."

"You did? How come?"

She looked at me curiously. "Because she's sick and all—and so's she'd feel better."

As we walked down the hill, I glanced sideways at Doreen under cover of my bangs. Imagine her praying for my aunt, and she didn't even know her! It hadn't occurred to me to pray for her in all the time she'd been with us. But then, I rationalized, Doreen was really more religious than I. If it hadn't been for her, I wouldn't have made nearly as many after-school visits to the church.

One day the year before when I was making one of these visits, as I knelt and prayed, I spotted a dime on the floor just under the kneeler. I hadn't been praying for money, but it was a welcome sight, and I reached down and picked it up. When I got home, I burst into the flat shouting:

"Ma. Look what I found."

"What is it dear?" she called from the kitchen.

I went down the hall to show her.

"A dime!" she marvelled. "Where did you find it?"

"In church."

"In church?" she repeated, her smile fading.

"Yep. I was kneeling there praying, and I just happened to look down, and there it was." At her look, I asked, "Why? What's the matter?"

"If you find money in church," she said, "you should put it in the poor box."

"Who said?"

"I don't know that anyone *said* it, but it's something I believe you should do. Maybe some child brought it for collection and dropped it before the plate came around. Or it might have fallen out of the collection plate."

I could see how that could happen. On Sundays, as the ushers reached the end of each aisle, they would dump the money they'd collected in the collection plate into a black velvet bag held by another usher, and some Sundays an usher would be a bit shaky, and a coin or two wouldn't make it into the bag.

"Do I hafta take it back?"

"I think you'd better."

"Aw gee. Do I hafta go now?" It was a Friday afternoon.

"No, you can wait and put it in the poor box on Sunday morning."

I considered having the dime burning a hole in my pocket for the rest of Friday and all day Saturday and knew I wasn't made of the stuff required for that kind of resistance to temptation, so I decided to take it back right then.

I walked back along Sherbrooke St., past the corner grocery with its assortment of fruits arranged temptingly and gleaming moistly in the window; past Laura Secord's candy store with its trays of chocolates; past the bakery shop that sold day-old goodies at half price and which had a sign over the cash register saying, "If you're satisfied, tell your friends, if not, please tell us"; past the Bluecrest Ice-Cream parlour that sold cone-shaped ice cream; past Nat's which sold mello-rolls; past Magid's which sold toys; and past Heller's which had a soda fountain.

I crossed over to the park where all the retired railroad men sat on a row of benches facing the funeral parlour across from them, and walked up the hill we slid down on our sleighs in the wintertime, past the clubhouse where we changed into our skates, across the baseball diamond, across the street and into the church.

Blessing myself with holy water as I went in, I went over to the poor box which was located at the back of the church behind a bank of candles. I considered spending the dime by lighting one of the candles, but that money only went to buy more candles, whereas the money in the poor box went directly to the poor. As I dropped the dime into the slot, it made a forlorn sort of clink as it hit a couple of other coins. There weren't many coins in the poor box in the nineteen-thirties.

We parochial school kids spent a good deal of time over at the church throughout the course of the school year.

We were always going over to have something or other blessed—water, rosaries, candles, holy pictures, medals, prayer books, palms for Palm Sunday and various other religious articles. On St. Blaise's day we even had our throats blessed. The priest did this by placing two crossed lighted candles under our chins and murmuring a prayer.

On Ash Wednesdays we went over to have a dab of black ash smudged on our foreheads to remind us of our humble beginnings, and our ignominious ultimate endings. And we went over to Confession on the first Thursday of every month, and to Mass and Communion on the first Friday. We returned to church on First Friday afternoons for the Benediction of the Blessed Sacrament.

It was invariably during the Divine Praises: "Blessed be God. Blessed be Jesus Christ, true God and true man. Blessed be the Name of Jesus," and so on, that poor Helen fainted and had to be helped out of church.

Another time she fainted was one Sunday after we had walked in a procession around N.D.G. behind our pastor who was carrying the Host aloft in its shining golden monstrance, followed by a raft of altar boys carrying flags, banners and candles. We girls were carrying baskets of rose petals which we tossed out on the street as we walked. It was one of the hottest days of the year, and we were dressed in navy blue serge dresses, long white stockings and white veils. The procession wound up at the church and was topped off by an interminable service. After sitting in the hot, stuffy church for what seemed like hours, Helen keeled over and was carried out by an usher.

I toyed briefly with the idea of pretending to faint so I could get out of there too, but didn't have the nerve.

Every Sunday we lined up in the school hall in ranks according to class, then were marched over in a body to the nine o'clock children's Mass, so that the entrances we made in church could be regimented.

The nuns gave us directions by means of a small wooden object that, when it was snapped shut, made a clacking sound. As we marched up the aisle of the church, when the nun wanted us to halt in front of our pews she clacked the clacker. When she wanted us to genuflect before entering the pews she clacked the clacker. And so that we wouldn't all bob up from our genuflections at different times, we waited until we heard the sound of the clacker again before getting up. Then we stood in our pews with the kneelers against our shins waiting for the next clack to tell us to kneel or sit. All through the Mass or Benediction service, we were guided to kneel, sit or stand by the sound of the clack, and we made our exit from the church with the clack in our ears too.

The year that we were in the first grade, which was the First Communion class, we spent most of our school days in church. That is, they taught us to read and write in the first half of the school year, but, from the time we returned from Christmas vacation till almost the end of the school year, all we did was practise for our First Communion day. We were taught how to walk with the measured tread of the truly devout; how to take the Host onto our tongues, and how to walk back from the Communion rail with eyes downcast and hands folded, without bumping into anything.

The requirements for our First Communion costumes were described to us in detail almost daily. The dresses were to be pure white, reaching below the knees, and having long sleeves. Our veils were to be pure white, and the bandeaux that held them in place on our heads were to be pure white as well. To complete this virginal costume, we had to wear white stockings and white shoes, with no article of any colour being seen on our person.

The parents of Depression kids didn't buy outfits that were going to be worn on only one occasion if they could borrow them, so my mother borrowed my First Communion costume from a friend of hers whose daughter had made her First Communion the year before, in another section of the city. I was dismayed to discover that embroidered on the bandeau that came with the veil was a series of tiny pink rosebuds. My mother's friend had embroidered them, and it had obviously been a labour of love.

The roses were so tiny and pretty, I couldn't bring myself to tell my mother they weren't regulation, so I wore the bandeau over my veil, hoping no one would notice.

Before the Mass, all of us seven-year-old First Communicants lined up in preparation for the formal procession down the aisle, and, as I stood in line, a nun stopped at my side and hissed, "What's that thing on your head?"

My hand went up to touch the offending bandeau, but the nun's hand was quicker than mine, and she snatched it from my head, unintentionally pulling my hair as she did so, which made me cry, and then she paraded me, still crying, down the side aisle to the pew where my mother was sitting in proud anticipation. Shoving the bandeau at my mother, the nun snapped, "She can't wear this. It has pink in it."

My mother took a hairpin from her own hair, placed it in the veil to keep it from slipping off, and dried my tears. Then, with no pink on me, but with red eyes, I made my First Communion.

We measured time as much by the liturgical calendar as by

the Royal Bank calendar on our classroom wall. We observed all the Fast, Abstinence and Ember days, and, if there was a hardship to endure, it was suggested to us that we "offer it up" as a sacrifice.

Certain foods were connected with the liturgy too. Traditionally, we ate fish on Fridays, pancakes on Shrove Tuesdays, gave up candy for Lent, ate hot cross buns on Good Fridays, and on Easter Sunday gobbled up chocolate eggs, roosters and bunnies to make up for the forty-day lack of sweets.

We had to call on all our resources of physical strength and stamina to withstand the output of energy required of us before Easter.

On Palm Sunday, the week before Easter, we stood perfectly still while the Passion of Our Lord was being read, a period of at least half an hour, and were admonished not to fidget under penalty of—well who knew what punishment was in store if you were caught moving?

On Holy Thursday, which was a school holiday, we were encouraged to visit seven different churches in order to gain a plenary indulgence, which meant that all the sins would be wiped from your soul and you could start again from scratch. You were supposed to walk from church to church, not ride, and you weren't supposed to speak as you walked, or, we were told, the plenary indulgence wouldn't go into effect.

The day after all that walking, on Good Friday, we fasted and made The Stations of the Cross. Some girls attempted to make them thirty-three times, once for each year of Our Lord's life.

Then, at the Good Friday afternoon service, we again stood motionless during the more than half hour reading of the Passion of Our Lord. When you're not supposed to move a muscle or eyeball, you find yourself with itches and twitches you've never had before. But we tried to be obedient, and to remember all we were told.

We were told that the Blessed Virgin cried every time a little Catholic girl whistled, chewed gum anywhere but in her own bedroom, showed her knees or bared her arms. And as I didn't want to offend the Virgin Mary, I wore a long-sleeved cardigan over my short-sleeved blouses and dresses, and clamped my hand over my mouth every time I found myself whistling, casting an anxious eye heavenward.

And we were told that as soon as we woke up in the morning, we should jump out of bed. Then in the next breath we were told, "The devil finds work for idle hands to do."

It was hard to keep track of all the different kinds of sins we were told about. There were the mortal sins and venial sins; sins of omission and sins of commission, the seven deadly sins, original sin, and other sins mentioned in the Ten Commandments so terrible, apparently, that no one would explain them. We gathered this because when the priest came to our classroom once a week to give us religious instruction, and asked the teacher which commandment we were studying, if she said either the "Thou shalt not commit adultery" one, or the "Thou shalt not covet thy neighbour's wife" one, he would clear his throat and say brightly, "Well then. Let's go on to the next one, shall we?"

The school auditorium served many purposes. It was used when we put on plays and concerts, for choir practice, assemblies, indoor recess, Sodality meetings, Girl Guide meetings, as a dining room for the kids who brought their lunch to school, and, because there was no gymnasium, for what little gym we had, which consisted of a few exercises given us once or twice a month by a flat-chested muscular lay teacher.

We did breathing exercises in our classroom daily, however. We would stand beside our desks, feet apart, and elbows tucked into our waists, then, at a signal from the wooden clacker, we would bend from the waist and yell, "ARRRRRRRGH!" This was supposed to clean out our lungs, although we may have spread some germs while doing it.

Besides lacking a gym, there was no library in the school, and the toilet paper was rationed.

Before recess, we were led class by class to the bathroom which housed several enclosed toilets, and a nun stationed by the door was the keeper of the toilet paper. If you wanted any, you had to ask her for it, and she'd peel off a couple of skimpy pieces of the slippery yellow stuff which wasn't any good anyway, and hand it to you. I was always too embarrassed to ask a nun for toilet paper, so I usually waited until I got home. Lots of other girls felt the same way about it, and there was much jiggling around as we raced through the Angelus, hoping to make it home in time.

If you put up your hand to "leave the room" during class, you were cross-examined:

"Yes?"

"May I please leave the room?"

"Number one or number two?"

"Number one."

"No. Sit down."

Next time:

"May I please leave the room?"

"Number one or number two?"

"Number two."

"No. Sit down."

Finally:

"May I please leave the room?"

"Number one or number two?"

"I think I'm going to throw up."

"All right, go then."

The school had a kitchen where we took our cooking lessons, learning to make rich pastries and other desserts, but nothing that would stand us in good stead should we ever have to prepare a meal. We also had our sewing lessons in the kitchen. We learned how to make a cat out of sateen and a pillow out of the same material for it to rest on. We embroidered a face on the head, stuffed the head with cotton batting, and put a zipper in the cat's stomach. The cat's body held your nightgown.

There was also a small music room, where a sweet-faced, sweet-voiced nun taught piano and singing for fifty cents a lesson.

One day this nun asked me to accompany her on her walk up the hill to the nuns' residence, as the nuns weren't allowed to walk on the street alone, and there was no other nun available to walk with her. While we walked, because I had always admired her serenity and gentleness of manner, and perhaps because my aunt had taught music too, I told her about the inconvenience I experienced in having my aunt living with us. When I was through, she sighed, and said, "Well dear, the best thing you can do is offer it up as a sacrifice."

When I tried to follow her advice, however, I must've gone about it in the wrong spirit, for I felt no less resentful and no more spiritually uplifted than before.

When we were taught music in our classroom, by our classroom teacher, there was no sound of music. We were taught to read music from our music books by placing the book on the desk in front of us, resting an elbow at the bottom of it, and beating out time by letting our hand fall on the book in a regular, rhythmic movement. We received hours of music instruction this way with never once hearing or singing any music.

Our elocution teacher wore a bright red wig and had an artificial eye—a combination we girls considered unbeatable. She visited the school once a week.

Another visitor was the school Inspector, who went from classroom to classroom wearing striped morning pants and a swallow-tailed coat. His name was Mr. Côté, so, inevitably, he was called Mr. Coattails, though not, to be sure, by the teachers, who blushed and fawned over him when he came into their classrooms. Naturally there were nicknames. Mother St. Stanislaus, for example, was never called anything but Mother St. Santa Claus. And Mother St. William, a nun with a pronounced overbite, was known as Buck Billy.

Other school visitors were two missionary nuns from China, who came to talk to us every year. We sat in the auditorium and listened, dismayed, as they told us how some Chinese drowned their baby girls. They said these babies could be bought from their parents for only ten cents, then brought to the Mission and baptized into the Church.

They concluded these talks by urging us to contribute as many dimes as we could towards the salvation of these pagan babies, and, for this purpose, they supplied a cardboard box which was placed on every teacher's desk.

It was one thing to be fired by a feeling of compassion for

those unfortunate babies, but to be able to translate that compassion into cold cash was something else.

With the missionary sisters' words ringing in my ears, I burst into the flat one day calling to my mother, "I've got to have ten cents."

"Ten cents? For what?"

"For a Chinese baby."

"I have no money to spare for Chinese babies."

"But Ma, if I don't get ten cents, a baby will be drowned!"

"Well then, offer up a prayer for it."

Sometimes the school day was lightened by entertainment.

On Valentine's Day, we always had a Valentine's party. There was a heart-covered mailbox on the teacher's desk to hold the Valentines we exchanged—even though it was an all-girl school—and, ironically, though in times of prosperity it may be considered an act of graciousness to give a homemade Valentine, during the Depression years Valentines had to be bought and many kids could ill afford them. So they made up excuses to explain why they'd neglected to bring Valentines to school.

One of the most creative stories offered one year was from a little Italian girl who came from a large family. She said she had put her Valentines into a paper bag, and, as she was crossing Sherbrooke St. with them, had dropped the bag onto the streetcar tracks and a streetcar had run over them.

In those years the nuns were treated to many inventive and imaginative tales, each explaining why a child had failed to bring money, or something that cost money, to school.

Whenever we had these class parties, we always had an "Amateur Hour" patterned after the Major Bowes radio show, and each child would be given the opportunity to sing, dance, recite or perform in some way. This proved to be a good outlet for show-offs, and equally good for kids who were shy, but could do some particular thing well.

My contribution to the entertainment had always been singing and yodelling, until the Valentine's Day the year before when I decided to tell a story instead.

I had been touched by the story I'd read about a twelve-year-old martyr named Narcissus who had suffered being stoned to death rather than relinquish the Host he was carrying for a priest during a period of religious persecution. So when it came my turn to perform, after a trio had sung "I'm an Old Cow Hand," I told this story, and not in what you might call a spellbinding style.

"Uh, there was this boy named Narcissus, and, uh, he was twelve years old? And, he had to carry this uh uh Host? For this um priest? Who . . . oh I forgot to tell you, it was when Catholics were being put to death and tortured and everything because they were Catholics and uh, where was I? Oh yes, well anyway. . . ."

When I finished, everyone looked sad. I had put a damper on the whole party. The act that followed mine just couldn't get off the ground. The teacher had been so moved by my story, she prevailed upon me to go from classroom to classroom telling it, so by the end of the afternoon I had managed to cast a pall over the entire school.

On March 17th, in addition to having a class party, we always took part in a St. Patrick's Day concert, for which we probably rehearsed longer and with more enthusiasm than would those performers in your average Broadway musical.

All of the parish priests were invited to these concerts, and were obliged to sit in the front row of the auditorium, where, calling upon awesome resources of self-control, they watched the proceedings straight-faced.

It's true that the corners of some priest's mouths sometimes twitched; that some priests were seized by almost uncontrollable coughing fits; and others sometimes had handkerchiefs half-obscuring their faces, but never once did they burst out laughing at the wrong moment.

Our school uniform was blue serge with white collars and cuffs and pearl buttons down the front, and whenever we had to take home a message such as, "Bring ten cents for the Chinese babies," we'd impale it on one of the buttons so we wouldn't forget. The message before the St. Patrick's Day concert read: "Wear clean, starched collars and cuffs, green hair ribbons and shamrocks."

Not being Irish, I had no particular feeling for St. Patrick one way or the other, but as she curled my hair with hot tongs, my mother tried to put me in the proper frame of mind for the concert by talking about her maternal grandfather. Ordinarily, though she had a musical voice, my mother spoke without a trace of any accent, but as she talked about my great-grandfather, her speech became softer and more lilting, and the letter "R" became more evident. By the time my hair was curled, the green hair ribbon in place, and my freshly starched collar had rubbed a red mark in my neck, she was sounding like Barry FitzGerald.

She told how my great-grandfather, Dennis Hunter, had come to Canada from Ireland in 1844, settled near Guelph, Ontario and married an Irish girl. Then she rhymed off the names of their thirteen children, and those of the wives and husbands of the ones who had survived and married, stressing the Irish names when she came to them. So, fortified with the knowledge of an Irish ancestor, and with all those Irish names still ringing in my ears, I was able to stand on the auditorium stage with my Irish schoolmates and sing Irish songs. And when we sang "When Irish Eyes Are Smiling," whether from my over-starched collar cutting into the burn on my neck from the curling tongs, or from my mother's newly-acquired brogue, I could feel my own eyes moistening over with a sentiment that could perhaps be described as "managed nostalgia."

My mother's relatives served her well whenever she had a lesson to teach or a point to make. Her father, Zaccheus Choate, was of the Canadian branch of the Choate family, but his American cousins were an illustrious lot of talkers: Joseph H. Choate, the lawyer, U.S. ambassador to Britain, and most popular after-dinner speaker of his time; Judge William Choate, another lawyer, and founder of The Choate School; and Rufus Choate, lawyer and orator, who, when eulogizing his friend and colleague, Daniel Webster, had the distinction of having spoken the longest sentence ever uttered. It had approximately 1,200 words in it, took about ten minutes to finish, and was, in fact, a comprehensive life of Webster covering his public service from 1813 to 1852.

Hardly a day went by, it seemed, that my mother didn't treat me to at least one Choate quote or anecdote. If I expressed a feeling of stage fright at having to stand in front of the class or the school and talk about something, she'd brush my fears aside with, "Nonsense. How could you be afraid to get up and speak when you have Choate blood in your veins?" So, with the Choate blood congealing somewhat in my veins, I'd get up and speak my piece.

One night at the beginning of the school year, I happened to mention at the dinner table that we were studying the War of 1812, and my father said, "You should ask your mother about that. She was there celebrating when they signed the Treaty of Ghent."

"Were you Mom?"

"Of course not. That's one of your father's jokes to illustrate that I'm no spring chicken—a clear-cut case of the pot calling the kettle black."

At that point, my aunt called out something from her room, and my mother said, "You'd better see what your aunt wants, dear."

My aunt's presence in the house had a fragmenting effect on our dinner-table conversation. From her room she could hear us, but we couldn't hear her, so when she called somebody had to get up from the table and go to her room to find out what she'd said, then return and tell everybody at the table.

That night I got up and went down the hall to her doorway and said, "Ma wants to know what you said."

"I said that Thomas Choate, your ancestor, fought in the War of 1812."

"Did he? Whose side was he on?"

"Why the Canadian side. He was with the Forty-ninth Regiment of British Regulars."

The Choates had come to Massachusetts from England in 1643, and my mother and aunt were proud of being ninth generation North Americans. They delighted in passing on stories of their forebears, which their father had passed on to them from his father.

"What did she say?" my mother asked, when I got back to the dining room.

"She said that Thomas Choate was in the War of 1812."

"Yes," my mother said. "He commanded his own company."

My aunt called out something again, and, without waiting to be asked, I pushed back my chair and went down the hall to her room.

"He didn't command his own company during the War of 1812. That was later, in the 1837 Rebellion. Have you learned about that?"

"No we haven't got that far yet." I went back and made my report, then asked, "How come he was fighting the Americans when he was born in the States?"

"It wasn't that he was 'fighting the Americans'," my mother objected. "It was that he was defending his hard-won home, and protecting his family."

"What do you mean, 'hard-won' home?"

"Well, he went through a great many hardships to establish his home in Canada. He started out in 1796 from his home in New Hampshire, *walking*, mind you, through the states of Vermont and New York, which were almost all unbroken wilderness at that time, until he found the place where he wanted to settle in Upper Canada, near Hamilton.

"He really *walked*?"

"Yes, he did."

"How far was it?"

"Oh—a good 500 miles, I would imagine."

"I wonder how long it took him."

"I don't know, but I know he made the trip several times, walking each way. In 1797 he cleared some land and planted corn and potatoes; then returned again in the fall to harvest them. Of course, he was a young man of twenty-three at that time. The last time young Thomas went home, he talked three of his brothers, and two of his cousins named Burnham, into going back to Canada with him.

My aunt called out something again, my mother nodded to me, and once more I went down the hall.

"Ask your mother to tell you about the smallpox and the crossing of the Niagara," she directed. So I did.

"Oh, yes. They had lots of adventures along the way. They left New Hampshire in early spring of 1798, taking a yoke of oxen, tools and provisions with them, and, by the time they reached the Mohawk River, their provisions were running low so they were anxious to get more. When they stopped at a house they found the people who lived there were sick with what turned out to be smallpox. So, since they'd been exposed to it, they decided to stay where they were until it was over. They rented a shanty, and inoculated themselves with the smallpox virus, and when they recovered continued on their way."

"Gee, you wouldn't think they'd know about inoculations in those days," I said.

"They knew a lot more than you'd think. Anyway, when they reached the Niagara River they found the stream above the Falls still frozen over, which meant they'd be able to cross the River on the ice. Since it was late in the day when they arrived they decided to wait until morning before crossing. But when they awoke, they found the ice they'd planned to cross had melted during the night."

"So what did they do?"

"One of the boys found an old flat-bottomed boat moored to the bank of the river, so they cut a long pole and lashed it across the boat, letting the ends of the pole extend over the sides. Then they drove the oxen into the river, fastened them to the ends of the poles and made them swim. This propelled the boat across, and they all arrived safely on the Canadian shore."

"Sounds like Swiss Family Robinson."

"People were resourceful in those days. When they got to the settlement, they started right in making homes for themselves. Every settler received a free grant of a hundred acres of land, and then could add to it by buying more. By 1812, Thomas Choate was married, had small children, and a good farm he'd worked hard for, so naturally when his family and land were threatened he defended them."

When my mother had finished speaking, I waited, fork poised, like the man waiting for the other shoe to drop, expecting my aunt to call out again, but my mother must have covered the story to her satisfaction because there was silence down the hall.

It was in this piecemeal fashion that I learned my Canadian and family history.

Shortly after school started, in order to see how well we remembered the words we had learned the year before, we had a spelling bee, and I was the last one left standing. The teacher called me up to receive my reward, and when I reached her desk she opened a drawer, drew out the prize and presented it to me with a flourish, saying, "Here you are—an all-day sucker." And she handed me the smallest lollipop I'd ever seen. I managed to thank her and make my way back to my desk with a straight face, but, as I slid into my seat, the girl next to me muttered, "Short day, wasn't it?"—which was a typical Jerry Colonna line, and I fell apart.

That wasn't the way they usually presented prizes. In most instances there were two prizes to choose from. One was something good, like a really nice holy picture, and the other something crummy, like a felt pen-wiper. The first prizewinner was told to make her choice first, and, as the rest of the class, including the second prizewinner and the teacher, watched, the first prizewinner's hand wavered over the good prize, then, to everyone's satisfaction but her own, she chose the crummy one. This was supposed to show how generous and self-sacrificing she was. As far as I could see, the only lesson to be learned was that it was better to come in second. I secretly admired a girl named Jacqueline, who, when confronted with a similar agonizing decision, chose the good prize, and the hell with it.

At the beginning of the school year we all had to take in two dollars to pay for some books, and, when it came time to pay, a girl named Mary Alice went out to the cloakroom to get the two dollars from her jacket pocket, then rushed back into the classroom shouting, "It's gone! My two dollars is gone!"

There was a collective sharp intake of breath as each child in the class empathized with anyone losing such a vast sum, and the teacher immediately turned to the class and asked, "Who took Mary Alice's two dollars?"

The question was greeted with complete, though fidgeting, silence. I could feel the blood draining from my face as everyone looked at everyone else suspiciously. Some girls blushed, while others, like me, looked sick. It was an uncomfortable feeling to know there was a thief among us and that each one of us was suspect.

The teacher tried again.

"Did anyone *see* Mary Alice's two dollars? Perhaps it dropped out of her pocket and someone picked it up?"

Silence.

"Jean," the teacher said to the door monitor, "Go to Mother Superior's office, and ask her to come here."

A collective intake of breath again. Mother Superior! When that forbidding figure came and heard the story, she left for a few minutes then came back with a roll of paper on which she told us to write our names, saying that she would be able to divine by how we wrote them who had stolen the two dollars.

When it was my turn to sign my name, my hand was wet and clammy and it trembled so I could hardly write. My only solace was in knowing that nobody would be able to make out the name, so they couldn't convict me.

As we wrote our names, Mary Alice sat watching us with her lips pursed and her eyes narrowed suspiciously. Having her two dollars stolen was clearly the most interesting thing that had happened to her. When Mother Superior finally left to study the scroll of names, we returned nervously to our schoolwork.

The next day, Mary Alice didn't come to school; we received no word from Mother Superior as to the identity of the culprit;

and no one as yet had confessed, so we did our work damp-palmed.

The following day Mary Alice came in late. We were all seated at our desks when she opened the door and dragged herself into the classroom, bumping her schoolbag against her calf and averting her face from the class.

She walked over to the teacher, handed her a note, then beat it out to the cloakroom and stayed there while the teacher read the note to herself and then to us.

It was from Mary Alice's mother, and it said that Mary Alice had been mistaken in saying the two dollars had been in her pocket. She had left it at home on the hall table. Then Mary Alice emerged from the cloakroom and took her seat.

Where before there had been a feeling of mass guilt, there was now a feeling of mass exoneration, and, as we settled back to work, a few nervous laughs rang out, particularly from two girls named Angela and Anita, the class gigglers.

The teacher had been forced to sit them as far apart as possible, but to no avail. They infected one another from across the classroom. They needed no humorous phrase or flash of wit to precipitate one of these journeys into hysteria. During a particularly unamusing arithmetic lesson for instance, Angela would titter at one side of the room, and Anita would hear her and erupt in giggles, which she'd try to suppress, making matters worse. Within a few seconds she would be sniggering and sobbing, her face getting redder and redder, until the teacher would bring them both up to the front of the class and place them one at either side of her desk.

The shame of this would cause them to bow their heads, and they'd stand that way for a while until Anita would raise her head ever so slightly and catch Angela's eye. Then they'd be off again.

Anyway, Angela and Anita got a big laugh out of the episode of Mary Alice's two dollars. They giggled and chortled and snuffled and snickered until they were doubled over in pain. And when Mary Alice said crossly, "I don't see what's so funny," that sent them off again and they had to clutch at their sides and gasp for mercy.

79

Not long after school started, I got the flu. If you were away from school sick for over a certain length of time, the school nurse came to visit you, which is what happened.

I was terribly ashamed to have her see that my bed was the couch in the living room. I had always liked her, and thought she was so pretty and everything, and now I was afraid she would go back and tell the nuns we were poor.

She was very nice about it when she was there, though.

My mother explained the circumstances regarding my sleeping in the living room, and I hung my head, not wanting to look the nurse in the eye. She didn't seem to notice how I felt, however, but looked around the room with interest. She asked who played the piano, and my mother told her my sister did, and that my aunt had been a music teacher.

Then she asked humorously who read all the books, and my mother told her it was my father, mostly. She looked at the grinning Billiken—The God of Things As They Ought To Be —on the mantel, then asked if the fireplace was real, and my mother told her no, it was fake. Then she spotted Napoleon and said, "My, what an impressive picture!" and I forgot my embarrassment for a moment as I told her proudly that my father had done it when he was only fifteen—which amazed her, as it did everyone.

But when I returned to school, I couldn't look directly at her again.

That year, because there were now six adults in our household, one of them invalid, all of whom had priority over the one bathroom in our flat, I had been late for school several times in a row, so, as a punishment, the teacher made me report to the first grade teacher every morning and afternoon before going to my own classroom.

When I went to the first grade on these occasions, the teacher had me compete in an arithmetic contest with the first graders.

She had written arithmetic problems, which she called "combinations," straight across the top of the blackboard, and I would stand on one side of the board, and a first grader would stand on the other side. Then, tapping each combination of numbers with a pointer as we came to it, we had to add up the sums as quickly as possible, and call out the answers. Whoever got to the middle of the blackboard first was the winner, and to my utter humiliation the first grader beat me every single time.

When I'd been a first grader myself I had always been beaten at this game, and had marvelled at the talents of two girls named Helen and Dorothy who were experts at it. But to have a first grader beat me now was the ultimate in humiliation. And the first graders weren't even good winners. They'd tuck their lower lips under their upper teeth and make "for shame" noises, which made me squirm all the more.

After about a month of this ignominy, I had a convulsion. I was in my parents' bed one evening, and began to shake so hard that my mother, who heard me from out in the dining room, came running in to see what was wrong, and had to pin me down by the shoulders to get me to stop shaking. She asked me what was bothering me and my teeth rattled so in my head I couldn't answer.

It wasn't until after she had gotten some warm tea into me (her remedy for everything) that I was able to get out the story of my daily humiliation. Then she wrote the teachers concerned a note, explaining the effect their punishment was having on me, and my enforced visits to the first grade came to an end.

One week of each school year was called Vocation Week, during which we were required to pray to be called to become nuns, but though I prayed along with the other girls I heard no call.

There was a World War I cannon in the park facing the school that was pointed in the school's direction, and beside it was a triangular pile of cannon balls. I often wondered, as I approached the school in the morning, if I'd find that sometime during the night someone had loaded the cannon and fired at the school. But it never happened.

Holidays

One day the tedium of school was broken when we were marched down the hill to the theatre on Sherbrooke St. to see the colour film of the Coronation of King George the Sixth.

Even though we were very young, we had been intrigued by the romantic reason behind the Coronation—Edward's abdication from the throne for the woman he loved. All the radio comedians at the time referred to the romance and abdication speech, and made hash of the phrase, "the woman I love."

We school children had arrived at the theatre too early for the Coronation film, and the feature movie was still on the screen. Whenever there was a love scene, all the girls would turn around and crane their necks to see how the nuns were taking it.

There was much giggling and poking of one another among the girls, but the nuns just sat with their faces expressionless, which was disappointing.

The monotony of school was also relieved by the occasional holiday, such as Teachers' Convention, Thanksgiving Day on the second Monday in October, and the big event of the autumn, Hallowe'en.

That fall, my school friends, Doreen, Anne Marie, Teresa, and I dressed up to go out as Dutch girls. We'd been in a school play called "The Pied Piper of Hamlin" the spring before, and our mothers had made our costumes for that, so we had to get more than one wearing out of them.

Under our Dutch caps we wore blonde wigs with long braids that we'd bought at the 5 & 10, and, decked out in this fashion, we took our baskets along Côté St. Antoine to ring doorbells.

Montreal kids always said "Charity please," when doors were opened to them on Hallowe'en, which my mother thought a demeaning expression. In Toronto they said, "Shell out." But since the other kids said "Charity please," that's what I said.

In some cases, before the person who opened the door would give you anything, you had to perform, and Anne Marie, Doreen, Teresa and I were well-prepared for this. We had a full repertoire. First we sang "Vieni, Vieni" followed by "The Lambeth Walk" which Anne Marie's older sisters had taught us how to do, and if the audience seemed appreciative I sang "Cowboy Jack" and then yodelled. I was the only kid in the entire school who could yodel, which was something of a distinction. When I finished yodelling, Doreen did a dramatic reading of all the lines she'd had in "The Pied Piper." Our big finish was a unison version of "With Plenty of Money and You."

Our act was such a hit at one place that the lady of the house put a quarter into each of our baskets, then invited us to come back later to entertain her party guests, which we did. We went over so big with them, they all dropped coins into our baskets too, and wouldn't let us go until I did a yodelling encore, and Doreen repeated her soliloquy from "The Pied Piper," which began dramatically, "Rats! They ate the dogs and killed the cats!"

We could hardly wait to get home to count our loot, and

when we did we discovered we'd made enough money to pay for a movie.

The day after Hallowe'en, being All Saints' Day, was a holiday for us, and while the ban on children under sixteen in theatres was supposed to be effective throughout Quebec, in the city of Verdun, which was a considerable distance from N.D.G., children were illegally admitted into some of the theatres. Somehow we managed to persuade our parents to allow us to make the journey there on our own. So, with a feeling of high adventure, we started out.

We took the streetcar to Atwater and St. Catherine, and then transferred to a bus which took us down Atwater and across the canal into Verdun.

Doreen was the leader of the excursion. While the rest of us tended to have our heads in the clouds, she always had her feet on the ground. She knew which streetcar to take and which corner to cross over to, and we followed her lead. My mother had cautioned me before I embarked on this foray to "Stick with the bunch."

When you don't see many movies, you're not picky. Any movie you happen to see is your favourite, and the performers in it are your favourite actors. For some time my favourite actors were Nelson Eddy and Jeanette MacDonald because the only times I got to see a movie it seemed their pictures were playing.

On this All Saints' Day however, a Shirley Temple movie was playing, which pleased us no end. We knew her so well it was like watching an old friend.

We wore Shirley Temple dresses, played with Shirley Temple dolls, cut out Shirley Temple paper dolls, crayoned in Shirley Temple colouring books, read all her movies in Shirley Temple Big Little books, had our hair curled like hers for birthday parties, and raised our voices in her songs: "The Good Ship Lollipop," "Animal Crackers in My Soup" and "At the Codfish Ball."

The movie that day was of the true Shirley Temple genre. She generally played an orphan or half-orphan, usually having a widowed father—Charles Farrell, Joel McCrae, James

Dunn or Jack Haley. And she was always looking for a new wife for him. She often found Alice Faye. Then Jack Haley and Alice Faye would have a falling out, and little Shirley would patch things up between them with a song, a dance and a flashing of dimples, and they'd both go off smiling, with little Shirley skipping joyfully between them.

When we left the theatre, I experienced the same sensations I always felt after watching a movie. First, the surprise of coming out into the daylight and seeing that life had been going on as usual, while I'd been transported to another world; then the feeling that every sound was muted.

The sound effects in real life didn't seem to be as sharp and clearly defined as they were on the screen. Footsteps didn't echo quite so hollowly; paper didn't rustle as crisply; nor did door latches click as distinctly. It was as if the movie was the reality, and life the imitation.

The other feeling I had was that I was in a movie myself— as if some unseen camera was grinding away, recording my every movement. As we walked to the bus stop, I found myself walking like Shirley Temple, and, as if following the instructions of an invisible director, executed a joyful skip every now and then. On the bus, I tried out pouting, dimpling, twinkling expressions on my fellow passengers, which sent them to examining the fingertips of their gloves, or reading the advertising cards over my head.

Before I went to sleep that night, I reviewed the movie we'd seen, putting myself in Shirley's role. Then, when I'd exhausted that bit of fantasy, I rewrote the movie in my head, leaving myself in Shirley's role of matchmaker, and putting my aunt in Alice Faye's role, and her former husband in James Dunn's part.

As I drifted off to sleep, I had gotten them back together again, and she had moved away.

Snow

The first snowfall that year occurred in the middle of the night and I was so intrigued by this happening, I celebrated the occasion by writing a poem about it:

The snow that falls in the daytime is all right,
But I like best the snow that falls at night.
When I wake up in the morning, rubbing my sleepy eyes,
I look out of the window, and get a glorious surprise.
The world is soft and deep and white
And all this happened in the night!
If I were Mother Nature, when winter rolled around
I'd wait until the nighttime to put snow upon the ground.

I knew that snow could be treacherous too, though.
The winter before, Mr. Shea, the school principal who lived

across the street, and father of six, including twins, came bursting out of his front door in the Dagwood Bumsteadian manner of fathers of six who live in one-bathroom flats. When he saw the first thick mantle of snow on his front porch, steps, and walk, he plunged back into the flat for a shovel; charged out again, and began shovelling furiously like someone in a speeded-up film. He had almost finished, when he slumped over the shovel, dead, at the age of forty-two.

It wasn't that there were more tragedies on our particular street in N.D.G. than on any other; but, when viewed through the eyes of a child, events of this type have a way of being indelibly stamped on one's memory.

The first snowfall ushered in the marble playing season. Only we called them smokies. My mother said they called them alleys in Toronto, and she couldn't understand why we waited until winter to play with them, since you can't wear mitts or gloves while you're playing. But even though we stood around with our right hands blue from the cold, and our forefingers chapped and worn nearly to the bone, we considered winter the best time for smokie playing, perhaps because it was easy to make a smokie hole in the snow with the heel of your overshoe, and to smooth a pathway between the smokie and the hole.

Sometimes our hands would get so cold, our fingers seemed to be permanently bent. But even though it would be dark out, and supper beckoned, if someone was having a winning streak we were loath to break up the game. Our fingers would eventually get beyond feeling. We'd scoop the snow-covered smokies from the hole and stuff them into our pockets, snow and all. While we waited our next turn, we'd hop from one foot to the other, trying to get our feet warm, and stuff our hands into our snow-filled pockets, to keep them from breaking off. Your fingers would finally become so numb, you'd start missing even the easiest shots. If I ever had a winning streak, it was always broken by Doreen, and I always left for home smokieless.

She was the champion. She had a mesh bag full of smokies

hanging on her bedroom doorknob that was so heavy she couldn't lift it. Her sister had been a crackerjack smokie player before her, and Doreen had fallen heir to all her sister's smokies as well as the ones she won herself, and she won from everybody.

In a futile attempt to keep up with her, I tried to cadge smokies from everyone. I went to retired smokie players and tried to get a handout, but discovered that even though they'd stopped playing smokies they liked to hang on to them as a reminder of their days of smokie-playing glory.

I used to get desperate for smokies. I got a nickel a week allowance, and I'd blow the whole thing on smokies, and promptly lose them to Doreen. Once I was so desperate, after having exhausted my allowance, my savings and the supply of empty milk bottles under the kitchen sink, I toyed with the idea of asking my aunt to stake me to my next smokie game, but lacked the nerve.

I finally asked a big boy down the street if he'd give me some of his old smokies, and, without much graciousness, he brought out a wooden peach basket full of them, and told me I could take three. So, with an equal lack of graciousness, I took a three-er and two fivers.

As soon as the cold weather set in, my mother got out my Red River coat for me to try on.

These coats were the winter costume of Quebec children. They were made of navy blue melton with red flannel lining, red trimmed epaulets, a narrow red stripe down the side seams and a navy blue Capuchin hood, lined with red. With the coat, we wore red woollen leggings, red mitts, and a red sash and toque, which lent the costume a dashing, habitant air.

But there was no dashing air about me as I stood in front of the full-length mirror in the entry hall while my mother tugged at the sleeves, willing them to come down to cover my wrist-bone. After a final fruitless tug which left my wrist exposed, she had me try on last year's mitts to see how well they covered the sleeve. But they had matted and shrunk in their last washing; Walter had stolen my toque; and my leggings, which we pulled on over our shoes and wore under black-buckled overshoes, had holes in the toes.

I stood looking into the mirror dolefully, and my mother's face behind me reflected my gloom.

Her face also looked different in the mirror than it did when you looked at it directly. I had noticed this phenomenon before. Anyone whose face I saw in the mirror always looked funny around the nose and mouth—sort of pinched in and peculiar.

It occurred to me that my own face in the mirror probably looked that way to other people too, and if it looked like that to other people, then it must be reflecting like that back to me, which meant that I had never really seen the way I actually looked.

It was one of those thoughts that tend to make your head ache, like seeing Orphan Annie on your Orphan Annie mug holding an Orphan Annie mug in her hand, which in turn. . . .

"We'll just have to take you downtown and buy you a new winter outfit," my mother said, jolting me out of my reverie, and I brightened immediately.

We waited till the following Saturday, when there would be someone home to look after my aunt, to go downtown.

When we were in Eaton's coat department, my mother asked, "Do you want another Red River coat, or something different?" What an odd question. We came home not only with a new Red River coat, but a new red toque, leggings, mitts and sash as well.

Because this outfit was worn by almost every kid in the school, we were always getting our toques, sashes and mitts mixed up with someone else's.

Shortly after I went to school in my new winter costume, I got my toque mixed up with that of a girl named Evelyn. I said she had my toque, and that the shabby, tacky toque left over was hers. She claimed the new one was hers and the old one was mine. We started the argument in the cloakroom, and one thing led to another until soon we were pulling each other's hair and the tassels off the toques. The fight was finally broken up by the teacher, who played the role of Solomon. I told her that I'd gotten a new toque that week, and if she didn't believe me she could phone my mother, and Evelyn finally admitted she was wearing the same toque she'd worn the year before, so the teacher examined the two toques and gave the newer-looking one to me and the faded one to Evelyn. Then she kept us in after school for fighting.

As we walked down the hill together later, because I was annoyed about being kept in after school, I confided to Evelyn, "If it wasn't a sin, I'd shoot the teacher."

As soon as I got to school the next morning, the teacher marched Evelyn and me outside the classroom and asked me, "Did you say that if it wasn't a sin, you'd shoot me?"

I stole a glance at Evelyn, but she studiously avoided looking my way.

"Yes," I mumbled.

"Yes what?"

"Yes, Mother."

"Do you know you committed a sin by merely *thinking* such a thing?"

"No."

"No what?"

"No, I didn't."

"Do you realize what a terrible sin it is to say such a thing about a religious?"

"No Mother."

"Get down on your knees and apologize."

I didn't move.

"Did you hear me?"

"Yes, Mother."

"Kneel down then."

I hung my head.

"I said, get down on those knees and apologize."

"I'll apologize," I said at last. "But I won't kneel down."

"How *dare* you? You'll get down on your knees young lady, or I'll know the reason why." So saying, she grabbed me by the shoulder, marched me back into the classroom and pointed to the platform her desk stood on. "Kneel there," she told me. "And you'll kneel there until you apologize."

I knelt, but I kept my lips sealed. I didn't mind the idea of apologizing but I couldn't bring myself to do it while on my knees. Conversely, I didn't mind kneeling as long as I didn't apologize.

This clash of wills went on for the rest of the week with me kneeling on the teacher's platform, missing my schoolwork and recess and shifting from one knee to the other, but not saying I was sorry. Over the weekend I told my mother about the situation. She sighed and said, "It would've been easier all around if you'd just apologized in the first place."

"I know," I said. "But it seemed like an awful thing to do."

"How do you mean, 'awful'?"

"Well"—I knew I was going to have trouble articulating how I felt—"it just doesn't seem right for a person to kneel down and apologize to another person. I mean, I could understand it if she had said for me to kneel down and apologize to *God*, but like for me to kneel down and apologize to *her*, that seemed like a sin."

My mother shook her head, "I'm afraid this is all too much for me. Let's go speak to your father about it."

We went into the living room and I told him what I'd told my mother. He listened carefully to what I had to say, then said to my mother, "She's perfectly right. It would be a sin against human dignity for her to kneel down and apologize." Then he patted my hand and said, "You don't have to kneel down to apologize to anyone—ever."

"But she said I'd have to kneel on her platform until I do."

"Well you won't."

"How come?"

"I'll write her a note. And you'll apologize to her, but you'll be standing with your shoulders back and your chin up and you'll look her in the eye."

And that's what happened. I didn't have to envy Elsie anymore. I had a father who could stand up to the nuns too.

When the snow fell there was always plenty to do in Montreal.

When it was brand new and still fresh and clean, you could

make angels in it by falling backwards and moving your arms back and forth in an arc to make wings. Then there was tobogganing and skiing.

You could take your toboggan into the streetcar and ride along Sherbrooke St. as far as Claremont, then get off and transfer to another car which took you up Claremont and along Westmount Avenue to Lansdowne where you got off and continued the rest of the way by foot to Murray Park, which had a toboggan slide that seemed miles long.

Or, you could take your skis with you and either ski at Murray Park, or stay on the streetcar and continue up Lansdowne to The Boulevard, and along that impressive thoroughfare until you came to the Glen Eagles apartments, which seemed to grow out of the mountainside, and get off and walk up Mount Royal Park to the ski area. And maybe after skiing all afternoon you'd warm up with some hot chocolate at the Chalet up by the Lookout. But because such exotic excursions cost money, most of the time you just skated or went sleigh riding at your local park.

If you were rich, you could take one of the horse-drawn sleighs for hire that stood outside the gates at McGill University, and across from the Windsor Hotel, up to the Lookout on top of the mountain. I never knew anyone who did it. (When there was no snow, horse-drawn calèches performed the same service. I never knew anyone who rode in them either, but I knew many who would have dearly loved to.)

The coming of snow also meant that Christmas was just around the corner, and from the first of December on that was all anybody thought about.

First there was the problem of deciding what to ask for. I pored over the ads in the *Star* every night. So many interesting things were being offered: there were motor boots, that is, black velvet overshoes with black fur down the front, which we kids called pussy boots, and thought so much classier than the buckled galoshes we usually wore. There were Shirley Temple dolls ranging in price from $2.98 for the 13" size to $6.98 for the 22" size—wearing a white dress with red polka dots like the one Shirley wore in "Stand Up and Cheer." Rubber rain-capes and tams were in style then; putt-putt boats were only ten cents, as were Big Little books. They had celluloid dolls for five cents each so you could get five and have your own quintuplets. They had muffs with zippered pockets in them; Mickey and Minnie Mouse watches for one dollar; Tootsie Toy metal doll-house furniture, which included, besides a sofa and two chairs with a plush finish, a metal radio with doors that opened, table lamps and tables. It was almost impossible to make up your mind about what you wanted. And then, of course, you had to do your own Christmas shopping.

My father was no problem to shop for. I bought him the same thing every year—a package of Old Chum pipe tobacco, which cost ten cents, and a package of pipe cleaners, which cost five. Though I gave him the same thing every Christmas, it always seemed to come as a surprise to him. He would invariably have just run out of tobacco, and, if not for my gift, would have been without a smoke on Christmas Day.

In addition to a tangible gift, every year we girls gave our mothers what our teachers called "a spiritual bouquet"—a card we decorated with flowers telling how many Masses, Holy Communions, Rosaries, church visits and Stations of the Cross we'd offered up for her during the course of the year.

The 5 & 10 was an exciting, bustling place before Christmas, with its red paper bells hanging around the store, and its tinsel-strewn counters.

They always got in a big batch of new Big Little books for the Christmas trade, and we kids spent hours at the counter reading them. The books told the story of current movies and had stills from the film on each facing page. The slogan on the cover admonished you to "Read the book, see the picture," and, since we couldn't see the picture, being able to read the book helped keep us *au courant* with what was happening on the old silver screen. But while I spent a good deal of time looking around Kresge's, I did my real Christmas shopping at Meyer's—for the personal touch.

Meyer's place was much more than a candy store. For its

size, it offered an amazing variety of goods and services. Outside the door was a bench on which were stacked the *Star*, *Gazette* and *Herald*, as well as a few French dailies, held down by heavy weights. People waiting for streetcars paid for the papers by tossing their pennies down on the stacks of papers —a temptation some Depression kids couldn't always resist.

Inside, there was a soda fountain, a wall of magazines, a glass cabinet full of smoking supplies: such things as pipe tobacco, and Guinea Gold, Grads and Turret cigarettes; greeting cards; the one-cent candy case; beyond that a small lending library; and, in the back of the store, an area of counters on which were arranged low-cost gift items for people with Christmas shopping budgets the like of mine.

A few days before Christmas I presented myself at the store, and told Mr. Meyer I'd come to do my Christmas shopping; that I had seventy cents to spend and six people to buy for. After getting the Old Chum and pipe cleaners purchase out of the way, I got down to business.

"I thought I'd give my mother a thimble, Mr. Meyer. I stepped on hers the other day and bent it."

"I have a few in the back with the thread. They're five cents."

"Five cents? I don't want to only spend five cents on my mother when I've spent fifteen cents on my father. I like my mother better, even."

"Maybe you could get some thread to go with the thimble?"

"That's a good idea. How much is the thread?"

"Five cents a spool."

"Okay. I'll get two spools of thread. One white and one blue. That's—thirty cents I spent. Now my brothers. I thought I'd spend ten cents each on them."

"How about these key rings? They're ten cents each."

"Okay. I'll get two—a red one and a yellow one. Let's see. . . . That all comes to fifty cents. Now I have two more gifts to get. One for my sister and one for my aunt."

As I moved down toward the back to the gift counters, something caught my eye.

"Oh look at the lovely salt and pepper set! How much is it?"

"Ten cents."

"Only ten cents? It's beautiful! Oh, I have to get *that*. I'll give that and the thimble to my mother instead of the thread. How much is this little glass kitten?"

"Ten cents."

"It's cute. I'll get it for my sister. Now let's see, I spent. . . ."

"You've got ten cents left, and a present to get for your aunt."

"I wouldn't spend the whole ten cents on *her*. I hate her."

"So why buy her a present?"

"I hafta. She lives with us. My mother would say I had no Christmas spirit if I didn't. I don't know what to get her though. She's sick in bed, and she doesn't do much. Can you think of anything?"

"Why don't you give *her* the pepper and salt set? That should show you have the Christmas spirit."

"And not to my mother?"

"Your mother would be using it when she put it on the tray and took it to your aunt's room."

"But it's *not* my aunt's room. It's *my* room. And *my* bed."

"So what do *I* know from Christmas spirit?" Meyer asked his invisible companion.

After further deliberation, I decided to give the two spools of thread to my aunt.

A soft, fleecy blanket of white covered Montreal on Christmas Eve, heightening the excitement.

Before going to bed, I brought out my pile of six gifts, and asked that they be placed under the tree when it was finished, then, once in bed, I could hear my mother, sister and father folding up the gate-leg table, and setting up the Christmas tree in the entry hall.

After the tree and other Christmas decorations were up, I heard drawers and closets being opened, stuff being brought up from the basement, and the sounds of wrapping being done at the dining-room table.

While all this activity was going on, at nine o'clock, Dicken's *A Christmas Carol* came on the radio and I strained my ears to hear it. That was the first time I had heard the story, and I quaked at the clanking of Marley's ghost, and my eyes grew moist at Scrooge's treatment of Bob Cratchit. No one had ever sounded meaner or stingier than Lionel Barrymore's Scrooge. And when I heard the fate that would befall someone with no Christmas spirit, I was filled with dread. What a relief it was when Scrooge awoke to find he had a second chance!

Before my mother and sister went off to Midnight Mass, they half-awakened me and led me past the tree to the living-room couch, making certain I didn't see anything as I walked through the hall. But after they left the house, I waited until my father was asleep, then jumped out of bed and ran out to the tree. Rummaging through the presents until I found the two I had wrapped for my mother and aunt, I switched the tags on them. When I got back into bed, I felt immeasurably better.

Mr. Meyer, it seemed, had known something about Christmas spirit after all.

The day after Christmas, *The Montreal Star* waxed almost poetic about the weather, with the words: "Montreal celebrated the type of Christmas that is found on the greeting cards. Fresh, new snow covered the old. It weighed down tree branches, and loaded house roofs. Brilliant sunshine and crisply cold air completed conditions that were perfect for 100,000 youngsters who wanted to try out new sleds and skis."

Just as a naturalist is supposed to be able to judge the age of bedrock, trees and fungus by counting the number of circles or lines in them, so too, could you tell how many snowfalls there'd been by counting the number of lines in the sides of the snowbanks piled high on either side of the street by the snowplough. That year, by Christmas, the snowbanks looked like *mille-feuilles*.

If you were standing near a snowbank talking to someone, both of you would automatically smooth a path in the snow the width of your overshoe. This was almost as good an aid to conversation as scab picking. As you talked, you rubbed your foot against the snowbank, reaching down occasionally to remove a cinder in the snow, then resumed your smoothing.

One day during Christmas vacation, while Margaret and I

were thus engaged having a conversation, Margaret mentioned that before Christmas, her mother had misplaced her address book. She had hunted high and low for it, but never found it. So she inquired around, and discovered that in one of the hotel lobbies downtown, there was a wide assortment of out-of-town directories of all the major cities in Canada. Margaret had moved to Montreal from Halifax, and most of the names they had to look up were in that city, so Margaret's mother went downtown and looked up all her friends' addresses in the Halifax phone book.

This information excited me.

"Do you know which hotel it was?" I asked.

"Yes, I went with her."

"Boy, is that ever terrific!"

"Why?"

" 'Cause we could go down there and look through those books and maybe find my aunt's husband and son's addresses."

"What do you want them for?"

"So I could write them and tell them she's sick, and wants to see them. Then maybe they'd feel sorry for her, and take her back home with them. That's what Doreen said."

"Hey, that's a *good* idea. But how would you know that you had the right people? I mean there could be a lot of people with the same name."

"I wouldn't know for sure about my uncle, but my cousin has a name I *know* no one else would have. My mother says it's because his first name is a family name that it's so different."

We began to plot our course of action. First, with Christmas just over, neither of us had any money, so we'd have to walk downtown from N.D.G.—a distance of some three or four miles. We'd have to dress warmly—wear two pair of mitts, and an extra pair of socks over our leggings.

We decided the following day would be a good time to go; leave early in the morning; take apples and cookies to sustain us along the way; and we'd be able to get home in time for a late lunch. We'd tell our mothers we were going sliding at

Murray Park (with our fingers crossed) which would account for the long time we'd be gone, but what could we do with our toboggans? We couldn't take them downtown with us, obviously. We enlisted Nancy's aid, and she agreed to keep them in her front hall till we got back.

So the next day, bright and early, we were on our way.

We walked straight along Sherbrooke St., then turned south at Guy to St. Catherine, stopping occasionally along the way at different stores to warm up.

The Christmas decorations were still up, of course, and would be till "little Christmas," January 6th, but somehow they had lost their magic. There was something a bit cheap and tawdry about the look of them now.

In one of the department store windows there was a life-size Santa Claus sitting on a gilt throne, whose head snapped back, arms flapped against its stomach and eyes lit up. A mechanical sound came over a loudspeaker outside the window so everyone on St. Catherine St. in the vicinity could hear it. "Ho-ho-ho." Then the head snapped back again, and the cycle was repeated. "Ho-ho-ho." The sound of this dogged merriment followed us as we continued along St. Catherine St., pausing every now and then to look at the stills outside the downtown movie houses. Some of the movies playing were: Shirley Temple and Jean Hersholt in "Heidi," at the Princess; The Ritz Brothers at the Imperial in "Life Begins in College"; Dorothy Lamour and Jon Hall in "The Hurricane"; and "Rosalie," with Nelson Eddy and Eleanor Powell at the Palace. We also stopped a moment to listen to the one-armed organ grinder in front of Eaton's, and watch as he touched the peak of his cap with the tip of his pinned-over sleeve each time someone dropped a coin on top of the machine.

When we reached Bleury St., Margaret decided we had come too far, so we turned around and retraced our steps along St. Catherine St., then turned north at Peel.

When we found the hotel we were looking for, we took the stairs in the lobby to a lower level, and stood looking at the rows of out-of-town telephone books, feeling slightly overwhelmed. But, after I sent up a swift, silent prayer to St.

Anthony that we'd find what we were looking for, we set to work, methodically looking through each one.

We'd been there for some time, and were beginning to become discouraged, when Margaret said with excitement, "Here it is! Her son lives in Winnipeg!"

"Let's see." I looked disbelievingly where her finger was pointing, and, sure enough, there was my cousin's name. There was no mistaking it. It gave me a funny feeling seeing it there. All steamed up, I wrote down the address and phone number on the paper I'd brought with me, and we continued looking through the other books for her husband's name, but didn't find it.

The prospect of walking back to N.D.G. loomed as a gloomy one. Our legs were tired from our long walk, so we waited at a streetcar stop with a crowd of people, and when a number three streetcar came along we lost ourselves in the crowd that surged onto it, and ducked past the conductor.

When we arrived back home, I slipped the paper between the pages of a book called *Pictures Every Child Should Know*, which my cousin, the schoolteacher, had sent me from Toronto for Christmas, then placed the book on top of the bookcase out of the way. I didn't want to rush into writing the letter, without thinking out carefully what I wanted to say.

The next day was one of those days when the snow is of the exact right consistency for making snowballs and snow forts. So I put on my Red River coat and two pair of mitts, and went out to make a snow fort on our front lawn. After a while, Louise, the little French girl next door, came out and started to half-heartedly shovel her front walk, pausing every now and then in her labours to watch as I started to build the walls of the fort. Noticing her apparent interest, I gestured to her to come over, so she did, and started to help me pack the snow. This was something we could do together without having to talk, and we worked for most of the afternoon until we had built an impressive fortress of snow, behind which we could hide after lobbing the snowballs we were piling up as ammunition against any enemy that might happen along.

Crouched behind the snow wall, rounding and making firmer the snowballs in our cache, we didn't see the enemy when he came along. It was Walter, the boy who had been hit by a car. The first we saw of him was when he leapt on the wall of our fort, crumbling it and covering us with snow. Louise and I jumped up yelling and he said, "Well, well, if it isn't the philosopher," and kicked down what remained of the wall. Then, to add injury to insult, he put snow in the hood of my coat and pulled it over my head, causing the snow to trickle down my neck. He was as one possessed as he danced on our pile of snowballs, squashing them and chanting at Louise, "French pea soup. French pea soup."

I picked up one of the snowballs that had eluded his feet, and, as he danced off down the street, I jumped up on the remains of the fort, made a flying leap and tackled him. I landed on his back, knocking him down. Then I pounded him on the head as hard as I could, and rubbed his face in snow, taking advantage of the fact that when I knocked him down I'd knocked the breath out of him. When he began to show signs of getting his wind back, I jumped up and ran back to Louise. He made as if to follow me, then apparently thought better of it, and continued down the street.

Louise said something derogatory about him in French, and I muttered darkly about him in English, and then she motioned for me to go home with her.

Mrs. Lalonde, Louise's mother, was a plump, jolly-looking woman, and, when she opened the door and saw our wet, snowy condition, she drew us inside and led the way out to the kitchen.

It was the first time I'd been in the flat since Mrs. Donovan lived there, and, though there was a tantalizing smell coming from the oven, it seemed as if I could still smell Mrs. Donovan's cats.

Louise's mother took our mitts and toques from us and spread them out on the radiator to dry, and, clucking sympathetically as Louise told her what had happened, she sat us down at the kitchen table, which was covered with seven or eight pies that smelled heavenly.

"*Tourtière*," she said to me, as she cut into one of the pies and gave us each a piece.

It was delicious. It was the first time I'd eaten *tourtière*, although I knew about them. I knew that French Canadians traditionally ate these meat pies on Christmas Eve after Mass, and on New Year's Eve, when they gathered together for a family party called "*le réveillon*." Mrs. Lalonde must have been preparing for such a party now. As I ate, I kept saying, "Is it ever *bonne*! *Très bonne*!" and Mrs. Lalonde and Louise smiled.

When I'd finished, I took my toque and mitts off the radiator, said "*Merci*," and left by the kitchen door, which was just across the driveway from ours. When I went in I told my mother about how good the tourtière had been.

"I've always wanted to know how to make a real French Canadian *tourtière*," she said.

"Why don't you ask Mrs. Lalonde for the recipe?" I asked.

"Does she speak English at all?" my mother asked. "We always wave hello to each other whenever we're out on our back porches at the same time, but we've never actually spoken."

Thinking back, I realized Mrs. Lalonde hadn't spoken a word of English the whole time I'd been there, but I hadn't noticed it at the time. All the sympathetic sounds she made as she took our wet things, the clucking she did as she listened to the story of nasty Walter, the beaming she did as I gobbled up her pie; all these things had been neither French nor English, but just the sounds mothers make in any language.

"No, she doesn't speak English," I had to reply.

"Well I couldn't very well get the recipe then," my mother said.

I had the feeling that if my mother had gone with me across the way and sampled some of Mrs. Lalonde's *tourtière* and said, "Mmmm," and had pointed to Mrs. Lalonde and then at the pie, and made pie-making motions, Mrs. Lalonde would have caught on to the fact that my mother wanted to know how to make one. Then they would have laughed and kept misunderstanding each other and had lots of fun, and my mother would have wound up knowing how to make *tourtière*. But I didn't try to put these thoughts into words, and, as it turned out, my mother, what with being busy with my aunt and all, never did get a chance to visit with Mrs. Lalonde. The Lalondes moved away the following May—perhaps because they hadn't been able to stand the lingering smell of Mrs. Donovan's cats.

Novena

After the New Year, on nine consecutive Friday evenings, my mother and I took a streetcar, with its foul, banana-smelling fumes, clear across the city to a church on Delorimier St. in the east end of Montreal. It was such a long ride, that by the time we returned home the backs of my legs were imprinted with the waffle pattern of the wicker seats.

We were making a Novena, that is, attending services consisting of special prayers honouring the Virgin Mary, asking her intercession for my aunt's recovery.

The first time we went, I asked my mother, as we were riding along on the streetcar, if she thought the Novena would work.

"You shouldn't speak of a Novena as 'working,' Mary. But something like this can only do your aunt good. What she needs now is the incentive to try to help herself get well. And

103

perhaps, after seeing us make this trip on her behalf each week, she might feel inspired to try to help herself."

"How can she do that?"

"She can do it by making the effort to get up; by walking around; by following her doctor's orders. She could do it by sitting down at the piano and seeing just what she can still do."

"Why doesn't she do it now?" I asked, feeling new resentment. I hadn't known she was capable of that much activity.

"I suppose she doesn't do it," my mother answered slowly, "because she really doesn't seem to have the desire to get well. She's convinced she'll never be able to teach again, and I think she's afraid to go back to Toronto without being able to make a living, so she stays in bed and doesn't even try to get better."

"What about her son?" I asked. "Do you think if he came to see her she might get better?"

My mother smiled sadly, "No dear, that's all over with. She hasn't seen her husband and son for years. Her son is a grown man now, you know, possibly married, with a family of his own. She lost track of them both years ago, as I told you."

At that, I decided to put out some feelers.

"Margaret said that before Christmas her mother lost her address book? So she went downtown to this hotel where they have all these telephone books from all the big cities in Canada?"

"Yes?"

"We were going to go down there some time and look for her husband's and son's names in the phone books, and if we found them we were going to take down their address. Then maybe we could write to them and tell them she's sick and would like to see them. And then maybe they'd feel sorry for her and take her to their place and look after her. Do you think that would be a good idea?"

"I think it was sweet of you and Margaret to think of it, but no, there are some things better left alone. This is one of them. After all, your aunt didn't get along with your uncle years ago when she was young and well, so there's no reason to suppose that now, when she's older and sick, they'd get along any better. Besides, they're divorced. He's no longer her husband, and for all I know he may be married again. No, it's best to let sleeping dogs lie. But it was nice of you and Margaret to be so interested in helping her."

I felt a stab of guilt at my mother's assumption that my interest had been altruistic rather than a scheme to get my bedroom back. Although the whole thing *would* have been like a Shirley Temple movie—me getting my aunt and uncle back together again after all those years, and their son standing between them, smiling—just like the way Shirley had reunited her mother with her grandfather in "The Little Colonel."

I imagined the scene as we went along on the streetcar. It helped take my mind off the fumes, which were making me sick to my stomach.

The streetcar was travelling along St. Catherine St. now, and we had crossed the St. Lawrence Boulevard, which meant we were now in the east end or French part of the city. Now all the street signs and store signs were in French. We had passed Ogilvy's, Simpson's, Eaton's and Morgan's department stores in the west end, and now we saw the huge French department store, *Dupuis Frères*, and *La Pharmacie Montréal*, the biggest drugstore in the world. Some signs outside snack bars read: *"Chien chaud," "Patates frites,"* and *"Buvez Pepsi!"*

Something my eye was always attracted to as I travelled around Montreal by streetcar, particularly in the French-speaking districts, was the beautiful, intricate ironwork that was used for fences, balcony railings, staircases, rooftop trim and over windows. It almost seemed that the poorer the district, the richer and more abundant the ironwork.

Eventually, we passed under the Jacques Cartier Bridge and turned north at Delorimier.

There weren't many people in the church, and most of them seemed to be from right around the neighbourhood. As I knelt beside my mother and listened to her praying with the rest of the congregation, I knew she wanted my aunt to get well as much as I did, but perhaps for different reasons.

When the nine weeks were up, and the Novena finished, I took to staring at my aunt every time I passed her room, looking for signs of a miracle, but nothing had happened. I respected my mother's dictum with regard to letting sleeping dogs lie, however, and, though I was dying to, I refrained from sending the letter.

Get-well card

As reliable a harbinger of spring as the crocus or robin were the young men from the Cheerio Company standing in front of the 5 & 10 on Sherbrooke St., demonstrating yo-yo's or bolo bats.

These demonstrations stimulated interest in buying, and, when practically every kid in Montreal owned a Cheerio yo-yo or bolo bat, the company held yo-yo or bolo championships in parks and playgrounds throughout the city.

Doreen, Anne Marie, Teresa and I always showed up for these contests. That spring our goal was to win the bolo champion sweater, which was blue, V-necked, sleeveless and bound in red and white with several red stars appliquèd on it, with the legend BOLO CHAMPION emblazoned across the front. I used to daydream about winning it: I would be walking along Sherbrooke St. wearing it, and people would look at me and say one to the other, "There goes one of the best bolo-batters in N.D.G." and I would pretend that I didn't notice their noticing me. We stood in line for hours, squinting against the sun, and hitting the rubber ball attached by elastic to the wooden paddle. To keep up our strength, the Kik company dispensed all the free Kik we could drink.

We entered every contest, gulping paper cups full of Kik between times. Then, when they'd exhausted the kids at the park in N.D.G., the Cheerio man who awarded the sweaters and the Kik truckdriver moved on to Westmount Park for still more contests. So, having been unsuccessful at the first park, we went to the next, the Kik jouncing in our stomachs as we ran. But alas, despite all our tries for it, none of us won a bolo champion sweater. Not even Doreen.

As the spring days got progressively balmier, my teacher complained of my being "in the moon" as she phrased it. I thought less and less about school, and more and more about the summer vacation ahead. But something was bothering me, so I brought it up at the dinner table one night.

After everyone had been served, I asked my mother who was going to look after my aunt when we went to Old Orchard Beach that summer.

Before answering, my mother gave me a look to remind me that my aunt was just down the hall from the dining room, as if I could forget, and then said quietly, "I don't see how we're going to be able to go away this summer, dear."

"You mean we can't go away at all?" I asked, with rising inflection.

My mother gave me another warning look.

"I don't see how we can, dear," my father said. "Your aunt couldn't make a trip like that, and she has to have someone to look after her. I can't hire a nurse and pay for a vacation too, so there's no other answer but to stay home."

"Why does she have to stay here anyway?" I demanded, my voice going still higher.

"That's enough," my mother said. "We'll discuss this later."

"Where?" I cried. "Where can we go where she can't hear

us? No place! She's always listening. We can't talk about anything. *I* know why you and Dad go on those long walks, even in the winter. It's so she won't hear you."

"That'll do," my mother said shortly.

I scraped back my chair, stood up and proclaimed dramatically, "I can't have *any* fun. I can't do *anything*. All my things are all over the house. I can't *find* anything. I can't listen to the *radio*. I can't bring my friends in. I haven't got a bedroom. I *hate* living here."

With that, I rushed out of the room looking for a place to cry. Not having a bed to flop down on, I ran down the hall to seek the refuge of the bathroom—and found it locked. My aunt was inside. Rushing back to the dining room in a frenzy, I wailed, "See? I can't even go to the *bathroom* around here."

The next day when I came in from school, shouting, as usual, the good news, "Ma! Ma! I'm home!" my mother's voice came back, "In your aunt's room dear."

I went down the hall and stood in the doorway. My mother was holding a spoonful of medicine and saying to my aunt, "Open up now and take it with a smile."

"Hi Ma," I said, then, grudgingly, I said hello to my aunt.

"Hello dear," my mother said. "I had no idea it was so late."

I studied my aunt surreptitiously from under my bangs as she swallowed the medicine. No sign of a miracle yet. She was still just as wan and pale and weak-looking as ever.

"I'm going to play on Sherbrooke St. Okay?" I asked. "We're going to ride Steinberg's bikes."

Steinberg's grocery store, which wasn't far from our street, made its deliveries by way of bicycles with carts in front of them, and, when these were standing idle in front of the store, we appropriated them and rode them around the wide sidewalk on Sherbrooke St.

Capping the medicine bottle, my mother said, "You won't be able to today, dear. Your teacher phoned and wants me to go up to see her, so you'll have to stay around the house in case your aunt wants anything."

I made a face, but decided not to complain too much since it was because of me that my mother had to go, and I knew she dreaded going as much as I hated having her go.

When my mother left, I took my roller skates, which needed adjusting, out onto the front steps, and started to work on them with my roller-skate key. I had to do something to keep busy because my stomach felt like a clenched fist.

I was worried about what the teacher was saying to my mother about me. I could picture in my mind just how the teacher and my mother looked as they sat in the nuns' residence, because Doreen, Anne Marie, Teresa and I had stopped by there on Hallowe'en, and I'd gotten a peek at the room where they received their visitors. There were about a dozen straight-backed chairs placed precisely around the room, with their front legs just touching the edge of the rug, and that seemed to be the extent of the furnishings. It was in one of these chairs that my mother had to sit and listen to stories about how bad and how dumb I was.

And the stories were true.

As soon as I went through the school door, invariably late, I became a smart-alecky, wise-cracking show-off, delighting in making the other kids laugh, and trying to best the teacher in arguments.

My mother had had these interviews with my teachers at least once a year, and she always came home bewildered, unable to reconcile the picture the nun painted of a loud-mouthed, bold little know-it-all with the relatively quiet, fairly obedient child I generally was at home.

The year before, my teacher had told my mother to make me stop playing with Doreen. She said Doreen was bold, and a bad influence on me. That's why we'd been split up this year, with Doreen continuing in the A class, and I in the B. That was the thing about being taught by nuns; they all lived in the same house and compared notes. I couldn't see what the teachers would have against Doreen though, other than the fact she was so smart, usually smarter than the teacher, even. She was always catching them in arithmetic mistakes, and always made certain to point them out.

One day she was crying as we walked home from school, and the reason for her tears was that she had made a mistake in arithmetic. It was the first time it had happened! Then, as it turned out, when Doreen's father went over the paper, he discovered she hadn't made a mistake after all. The teacher had.

Doreen and I sometimes wished we had Irish surnames. You could get away with a lot with the nuns if you had an Irish name. They also liked you if you were rich. Another thing they liked was long, blonde hair. So, if you were Irish and rich and had long blonde hair, you were in.

Something else that went over big with them was if you were part of a large family. If you came in one morning and said your mother had had a baby the day before, they'd be nice to you all day. And if you had a relative who was a nun or a priest or even a Brother you could do no wrong.

One of the many ways *I* irritated my teachers, was by repeating in a scornful whisper any word they mispronounced. I knew the words were being mispronounced because, whenever I pronounced them at home the way my teachers pronounced them, my father corrected me. For instance, one evening at the dinner table I announced, "Mary Ellen talked after the bell, so we had to say another decket of the beads."

My father looked up and said, "Another what?"

"Another decket."

"What's that?"

Since my father was a Protestant, and not familiar with such things, I explained patiently, "A decket is ten beads."

"Why should ten beads be called that?"

"The teacher says because decket means ten."

"Decket means ten? You mean de*cade*."

"The teacher says 'decket,' and so does the priest when he gives me penance."

"Well they're wrong."

"Dear . . . ," my mother gave him a silencing look, but he was not to be silenced.

"Well they *are* wrong, dammit," he said irritably. "I'm not having them tell any child of mine that D-E-C-A-D-E is pronounced decket. That's ridiculous. Don't they know how to speak at that school?"

111

"Well you might call it a Catholic pronunciation," my mother suggested, tentatively.

"Oh, does each religion have its own particular way of pronouncing words now? I wasn't aware of that. And is decade the Protestant pronunciation of D-E-C-A-D-E? I wonder what the Jewish pronunciation is. Not to mention the Hindu. And what does Confucius say?" When my father got something like that going he played with it like a pup with a rag in its teeth.

Another time I said, "Pat's brother is going to Lyola next year."

"He's going where?"

"Lyola."

"Where's that?"

"You know. On Sherbrooke St. in Montreal West. *You* know."

"I know there's a school there called *Loy*ola."

"Our teacher says Lyola. And so does the priest. And he went there, even."

My father gave me such a look, I didn't say Lyola again.

Some more of the nuns' favourite mispronunciations were grievious for grievous, immedjitly for immediately, insefferable for inseparable, and the one that sent my father off on another of his tangents, extramunction for Extreme Unction.

I was also critical of the way we were taught certain subjects, such as poetry. When we studied "The Highwayman," for instance, because it was a long poem each child in the class was required to read three or four lines aloud in sequence, which, for a rhythmic poem like "The Highwayman," or any poem for that matter, was disastrous.

We had fast readers, slow readers, good readers and bad readers, and this motley crew conspired to dispel any interest we might have had in the poem. To make matters worse, when it came my turn to read, my lines were the climax of the poem and one of the words I had to say was "breast," I was so embarrassed at having to say such a word in front of a nun that I mumbled the whole stanza.

With our halting, mumbling, fumble-tongued reading we

managed to fell "The Highwayman" and Alfred Noyes with one blow. We performed the same hatchet job on Sir Walter Scott, Rudyard Kipling, Tennyson and Longfellow. And each time we laid low another poet, I complained about having to read poetry aloud that way.

Besides telling about my bad conduct, I imagined the teacher was probably giving my mother an earful about how hopeless I was in arithmetic. It was my worst subject.

The teacher spent ten or fifteen minutes of every arithmetic period bending over my desk trying to explain some problem to me. I listened intently for a while, but never understood a word she said. She could just as well have been speaking another language. My mind would begin to wander and I'd think about something else, then, when she began to look as if she were about to reach her exasperation threshold, I'd say I understood. Then she'd pass on to a girl named Woody, who was as dense in the subject as I.

Another subject I had difficulty with was French. The French we were taught and the way we were taught it didn't help us toward ever carrying on a conversation with a French person in Quebec. The only kids I knew who did well in the subject were those who had either a French maid or a French parent.

An old-fashioned phonograph, old-fashioned, that is, even then, was brought into the classroom, and after the machine had been wound up a metallic voice would admonish us to "répéter après moi," and we recited the words after the man, trying our best to imitate his Parisian inflections and accent, which didn't sound a bit like our French Canadian butcher and dentist.

The fact that I lay awake every evening after going to my parents' bed, listening to the radio, probably did nothing to enhance my scholarship either. I just couldn't bear to miss "The Eddie Cantor Show," Fred Allen's "Town Hall," Rudy Vallee, Bing Crosby's "Kraft Music Hall," "Hollywood Mardi Gras" with Charles Butterworth, and "The Lux Radio Theatre."

I always tingled in anticipation when Cecil B. DeMille's

resonant voice enunciated, "Lux presents–Hall-ee-wood!" and forced myself to stay awake until he came back at the conclusion of the hour to tell what play he had in store for the following week. As I listened, I couldn't help wondering why the next week's offering always sounded more promising than the one I'd just heard.

I was also taken with a show called "Big Town," which featured Edward G. Robinson as Steve Wilson, managing editor of *The Illustrated Press*, who was "feared by racketeers," and Claire Trevor as Lorelei Kilbourne, his star reporter. I liked it especially since I intended to be a newspaperwoman like Lorelei when I grew up. Once I asked my father if working at *The Montreal Star* was the same as *The Illustrated Press* and he didn't even reply; he just laughed.

While I sat on the front steps working on my roller skates and worrying about what was being said at the nuns' residence, Margaret came down the street bouncing a lacrosse ball.

"Hi," she said, pausing in front of our flat and bouncing the ball.

"Hi," I answered.

"Whatcha doin'?"

"Minding."

"Your aunt?"

"Yes. New ball?"

"Yep. Just got it."

She bounced it, counting, "One, two, three, alary, four, five, six, alary, seven, eight, nine, alary, ten alary, postman."

That was just to warm up for a more complicated feat of coordination.

She tossed the ball in the air. "Plains," she said, before catching it. She tossed it again. "Cross," she said, crossing her arms over her chest before catching it. "Rollie-pollie," she said, making a rolling motion with her arms before catching it. "Backsie-frontsie," she said, clapping her hands behind her back, and in front of her before catching it. "Frontsie-backsie," she said, doing the same thing again, in reverse.

When she was finished, she sat down on the bottom step.

"Feel like doing anything?" she asked.

"I have to stay around the house," I reminded her.

We sat there a while, she bouncing her new ball, and I trying to fix my skates, and then she suggested, "Let's make phone calls."

"Let's," I agreed. "We haven't done that in ages."

We jumped up and went inside and I asked, "Who should we call? Mr. Meyer?"

Margaret nodded, her eyes dancing, and I consulted the phone book for the number of his store. When I found it, I dialed, and Margaret pressed her ear to the phone so she could hear too.

We listened to the phone ringing, and then Meyer's voice said, "Meyer's Candy Store." I asked quickly, "Have you got Prince Albert in the can?"

There was a pause, then Meyer replied, sounding resigned, "Yes." And I said, "Well please let him out." I hung up and Margaret and I doubled over with laughter. Then Margaret said, "Now it's my turn." She dialed Meyer's number again and when he answered, she said, "Does the streetcar run in front of your store?" When Meyer said, "Yes," shortly, she said, "Well tell it to walk. I want to catch it."

After hanging up, she asked, "Do you want to phone him again?"

"I haven't got the nerve," I said, shaking my head.

"I will then," she said, and dialed.

Mr. Meyer picked up the phone on the first ring, sounding annoyed.

"Meyer's Candy Store," he barked. And Margaret asked, "Do you have a streetlight in front of your store?"

"This is Margaret, down the street, isn't it?" Meyer said. Margaret's grin faded. "Yes, Mr. Meyer," she admitted.

"Does your mother know you're making these calls?"

"No, Mr. Meyer."

"Do you want I should tell her?"

"Oh no, Mr. Meyer. Don't do that. She'd *kill* me."

"Listen. You phone me once more and your mother's going to know about it. You hear me?"

Margaret swallowed. "Yes, Mr. Meyer. Good-bye Mr. Meyer."

She replaced the receiver gently in its cradle, looking chastened.

"I want to phone somebody else and do the radio station one," I said, and, at that, my aunt called, "Stop acting silly and leave the phone alone."

"We weren't doing anything," I protested.

"You're just tying up the line for a lot of nonsense. Why don't you go out and sit on the front steps?"

"Aaaaaaaaaaaall right," I groaned, and Margaret and I went outside, making an unnecessary amount of noise as we did so.

"Boy!" Margaret said, "You can't have *any* fun with *her* around!"

"It's the same thing with everything," I told her. Then I mimicked, " 'You've got the radio too loud. Do you *have* to whistle? *Must* you slam the door?' I can't do *anything*. And she's always listening to everything we say. She's got ears like a hawk. She's forever calling from her bed when she hears us talking at the table and putting in her two cents' worth. It gets to be a pain in the neck. Some nights we hardly say anything at the table anymore. Not only that, but because of her we're not going to be able to go away this summer. I wish to heck she'd get well and go back to Toronto."

We sat morosely for a while with our chins in our hands and with vacant expressions, when Margaret said mischievously, "If you wish she'd get well, why don't you send her a 'get well' card?"

I was puzzled. "Why would I do that?"

"It would be funny, don't you see?" Margaret explained. "If, after all the bother she's been to you, you sent her a get well card, it would make her feel her neck for being so mean to you. And she'd think you want her to get well because you're sorry she's sick, but you just want her to get well so she'll get the heck out of your bed. See? That would be the joke. Get it?"

I thought about it for a moment, then said, "It might be a good trick at that. But I haven't any money."

"How about cashing in some bottles?" she suggested.

So I went back into the flat for the bottles, and, as I tried to sneak them past my aunt's room, she heard them clinking, and called out, "What's that you've got there?" and I replied, "Just some milk bottles."

"What are you going to do with them?"

"Cash them in."

"I don't think your mother would like it."

"I'll explain it to her when she gets back. Margaret and I are just going up to Meyer's for a few minutes. We won't be long." So saying, I went out quickly, slamming the door behind me.

A few minutes later I set the bottles down on the cooler in Meyer's store, and told him casually, "I'm cashing these in." I'd passed the point of explanations regarding bottles. He knew I hadn't bought the milk from him, and I knew he knew. The days of pretence between us were over.

Margaret avoided his glance as we went down toward the rear of the store where the cards were displayed. We read the messages silently for a while, then Margaret said in disgust, "They all sound as if she's your best friend in the world or something."

I had noticed that too. I was looking for a card that would say simply that the sender hoped the recipient would get well soon, but the messages were so flowery that I knew my aunt would know the sentiments expressed weren't genuine. So even though it sounded as if I'd just heard she was sick, when she'd been sick in my bed for months, I finally settled on one that said:

Awf'lly sorry to hear you're sick
Hope you're well again pretty quick.

After borrowing Mr. Meyer's fountain pen to write the message, which, after much snickering, we decided should be, "from your loving niece," I signed my name, and we went to the post office to stamp and mail it.

Every day in every way

The next day I got the shock of my life. When I came in from school, my aunt was in the living room, sitting at the piano! The miracle had happened! She was trying to do some finger exercises—and not having much luck with them, by the sound of it.

When she saw me, she said, "Thank you very much for your card, dear."

I had forgotten about the card, and, at the mention of it, felt myself blushing as I mumbled, "Don't mention it," wishing she hadn't.

Not stopping to discuss it further, I continued on out to the kitchen as she resumed her practising.

She had been lying in bed for months, getting up only to go to the bathroom, or to sit by her window for a brief period each day as my mother made her bed, and now here she was up and sitting at the piano! I couldn't get over it. As soon as I reached the kitchen, I asked my mother about it.

"I think we might have you to thank for that, dear," she told me.

"Me?"

"Yes. You know I've been trying to get her to attempt to walk and play the piano for months, but she's always said she couldn't. But today, after your card came, she decided to try."

I didn't know what to say, so I busied myself pouring a glass of milk.

"It was nice of you to send her a card, Mary," my mother said. "I know all this hasn't been easy for you."

I was beginning to feel uncomfortable, and didn't want to hear any more of that kind of talk, so I drank my milk quickly and went and changed out of my school uniform.

One balmy day in late spring, Margaret and I were sitting on the front steps when we heard discordant sounds coming through the open living-room window.

Covering her ears with her hands, Margaret said, "Who's murdering the piano?"

"That's my aunt."

"I thought you said she made her living by giving piano lessons. She sounds like she needs some herself."

"I know," I said. "Isn't it terrible? She says she can't make her fingers do what she wants them to do."

"Why does she play then?"

"She figures the more she uses her fingers, the better they'll get. She doesn't sound any better though. But ever since I sent her that card, she's been trying to get better. Every day she practises walking. First it was up and down the hall, a little bit each day, now she walks up and down the back porch—back and forth, back and forth. The neighbours must think she's coo-coo."

"Why does she do it?"

"My mother says to get the fresh air, and so she can learn to walk normally after her stroke and being in bed so long."

"Do you think it's because of the card that she does all this?" Margaret wanted to know.

"I don't know," I said, feeling uncomfortable, "I really don't know."

"I bet it is."

"Well it doesn't *have* to be just because of that. I mean the doctor came to see her every week you know, and talked to her, and gave her shots and medicine and things like that. And don't forget my mother and I made that Novena for her. So maybe the card only had a little bit to do with it."

"I think it had *everything* to do with it," Margaret said, nodding sagely.

"Well I don't," I said, not caring for the turn the conversation had taken.

It wasn't long after my mother had her interview with my teacher that I had the second shock of my life—at report card time.

Reports were given out once a month, and presented in sequence. The child who came first received her report card first, and so on. That month I sat at my desk while the thirty-nine other girls in the class went up to get their reports ahead of me. I was the last in the class of forty to receive one.

As each name was called out ahead of mine, I slid down a little further in my seat, and when all the names but mine had been called I was slumped so low I was almost supine. But I couldn't make myself invisible, and when my name was called I unwound myself from the seat reluctantly and slowly made my way up to the front of the class. As I reached her desk, the teacher made a speech to the rest of the class, which I listened to with the thirty-nine pairs of eyes trained on me.

She told the others that because I disrupted the class so much with my comments about what we were being taught, and the way we were being taught it, and by my contradicting and attempts to make them laugh, she didn't want any of them to speak to me, walk home with me, play with me at recess or after school, or in any way communicate with me or acknowledge my presence for the next full month. Then she handed me my card, and I made my way back to my desk, trying my best to look uncaring.

But I did care. For the next month I felt the way the girls in the British girls boarding school books must've felt, when they were sent to Coventry. I still walked to and from school with Doreen, because, being in the other class, she wasn't obliged to honour my teacher's dictum, but as soon as we parted at our respective classroom doors I was alone until it was time to walk home.

When I got home, I sat at the gate-leg table every afternoon after school, studying, pausing only to listen to "Little Orphan Annie" at 5:45; and, when the older of my two brothers came home with the *New York Daily Mirror*, to read "Li'l Abner" and "Mickey Mouse," the "sallies in our alley" in Walter Winchell's column, then to turn to Nick Kenny to see what well-known people were celebrating birthdays.

I didn't tell my mother about my ostracism because I was too embarrassed about it, so she took my new study habits as evidence that I'd turned over a new academic leaf after the shock of coming last.

The following month I came seventh, which was something of a triumph, but it had been a lonely month.

After that, my teacher and I had an armed truce until the day I took one of my mother's corset stays to school. By bending it between thumb and forefinger, and then releasing it, I was able to send it clear across the schoolyard during recess. But as I was coming down the stairs at the end of the day, with the stay in my hand at the ready, with remarkably unfortunate timing I released the stay just as the teacher was walking past, and it hit her on the back of the head making a "ping" sound against her starched coif.

She whirled around, grabbed me by the shoulder and marched me back upstairs to the classroom, where, still fuming she snapped, "You think you're cute, but you're bold. And that's what you're going to write fifty times before you leave here." So saying, she angrily scrawled across the top of a sheet of paper: "I think I'm cut but I'm bold." In her swivet, she had neglected to put the letter "e" at the end of the word "cut."

I faithfully copied the sentence just the way she had written it, and when she saw this impertinence she made me copy the sentence correctly an additional fifty times.

I took heart, however, in the knowledge that the school year was drawing to a close and I'd have the whole summer to do as I pleased. My next year's teacher would be a lay teacher, which meant my mother would be spared her trips to the nuns' residence. She'd be able to go directly to the school instead.

Transition

One day in early summer, when I came home from the park, my mother and aunt were sitting in the dining room listening to "Between the Book Ends." As Ted Malone read poetry, my mother darned and my aunt knitted; her fingers were strong enough for this now, though she couldn't knit as quickly as she once had. As I came in my mother said, "You're just the person I want to see."

"Why?" I asked, guiltily. I always felt guilty when somebody said something like that to me.

"Your aunt feels she's ready to walk as far as the corner."

"Oh?" I said, wondering what this had to do with me.

"Yes," my mother went on brightly. "And since it'll be her first time, I'd like you to go along with her."

I was about to make an excuse to get out of going, but caught my mother's silencing look.

"Okay," I said sullenly, and managed to give my mother a put-upon look as I walked behind my aunt out the door.

I suppose I walked too quickly for her, because she asked me to slow down a bit. When I did, she had to take hold of my arm occasionally to steady herself. I was afraid people would think she was drunk, and hoped we wouldn't meet anyone I knew. But she seemed oblivious of my discomfort, and looked quite pleased with herself when we got back.

It was only when she was at the piano that she showed any signs of despair. She still couldn't seem to get her fingers to do what she wanted them to. When she played, discordant sounds still came from the living room, and one day, after attempting to play a more ambitious piece than her stiff fingers were ready for, she stopped abruptly. I happened to be passing through the entry hall on the way out, and, for once, her sensitive hearing failed her for she didn't know I was there.

I turned to glance into the living room and saw her sitting at the piano with her face in her hands and her shoulders shaking, and I stood there a moment watching. I supposed that at one time she would have been able to play the piece she was attempting now with one hand tied behind her back.

As I continued on out of the house, the playing resumed and I could almost hear her determination as she struck the keys.

As the summer progressed, we girls developed new interests. Boys were one. But they didn't show any interest in us in any overt way. If they did speak to us, it was usually by way of insult. "How much do you charge to curdle milk?" they'd ask. Or, "What kind of a noise does the wind make as it whistles through the hole in your head?" Or, "Is that your nose or are you eating a banana?" Or, "Is that your face or are you breaking it in for a monkey?" When a boy said something like that to us, we were suffused with a soft, warm glow.

We learned more about sex, too. One day Margaret found, in her mother's night-table drawer, a book called *Happiness in Marriage*, by Margaret Sanger. One afternoon when her mother was out, we pored over the contents of the book from cover to cover. It was certainly an eyeopener, but I still couldn't bring myself to believe everything in it. For one thing, I wasn't too convinced of Mrs. Sanger's authority on the subject. She didn't really seem to know as much about it as the girls we sat with on the front steps.

We also started borrowing books from the lending library near the park. The books rented for two cents a day, with a minimum rate of four cents, so together we'd take out two books, read a book a day, then exchange books. That way we managed to con the library out of two books for the price of one, and in the process, became fast readers. We even got so that we could read faster than the "Reading Time" estimated in *Liberty* magazine.

We were particularly interested in the literary output of a British novelist named Maisie Grieg, whose heroines invariably had Titian hair; applied their lipstick from "squat, golden tubes"; and became so agitated that their "fingernails bit into their palms," or they "bit their lips until they tasted blood." And they always drank water from a jelly glass. Even the titles of her books had a certain similarity: One was called *Bad Girl Leaves Town*, and another: *Good Girl Comes to Town*.

The men were usually named Jason or Nigel, and were sardonic, which we considered a romantic thing for a man to be. There was something the heroines were always threatening to do that puzzled us. They were forever debating with themselves about "throwing their cap over the mill." We wished one of them would finally do it, so we'd find out what the expression meant, but they never did. Since the stories were based in England, we concluded that throwing her cap over the mill must be something peculiar to a British girl.

Meanwhile, as we read, and talked about boys and sex, my aunt was gaining in strength and confidence each day, so much so that she felt she'd be ready to teach again by the fall. One day she wrote to the music school in Toronto where she had formerly taught to ask about the possibility of getting her teaching job back.

Then the waiting period began.

The mailman came twice a day, and before each delivery she stayed around the front of the flat, waiting for a letter.

Finally it came. I was in the dining room having a dress fitting when it arrived. She ripped the envelope open and read the letter over quickly, then looked up, her face flushed with excitement.

"They say they'll be happy to have me back teaching in the fall," she told my mother. "Isn't that *wonderful?*"

"It's *marvellous*," my mother said, just as excited.

My aunt reread the letter more carefully, then kissed it. "Oh, you don't know what this *means* to me," she said.

"I can imagine—like starting life all over again."

"Exactly."

I hadn't said anything throughout this exchange, until my mother asked, "Aren't you happy for your aunt, dear?" and I stammered, "Yes, yes. I think it's nice you got your job back, and all." And that I'll be getting my room back, and all, I appended silently.

The Saturday before my aunt was to leave, she and my mother went downtown to do some shopping, and I helped my father make the supper. We were having steak and onions, and whenever we had steak my father prepared it. He said he wouldn't trust my mother alone in the same room with a piece of raw steak because she'd cook it to death. This day, he was making the whole meal, so I peeled the potatoes for him.

As he peeled the onions, he said conversationally, "Well dear, it won't be long before everything will be back to normal again, now that your aunt is better."

I nodded, then, as I pared the potatoes, I said, "It was funny about that get well card."

"What get well card?"

"*You* know. I sent her a get well card last spring."

"Oh did you?" my father looked vague. "That was nice, dear. Oh yes, I guess I remember something about a card. What was funny about it?"

"Well it was right after I sent it that she started trying to walk and play the piano."

"It was? You don't say." My father was blinking his eyes from the onion and turning his head aside.

"I think maybe the card made her decide to get better," I said.

"Isn't that nice?" my father said absently, still bothered by the onion.

"The thing of it is," I went on, *bless me, father, for I have sinned,* "I sent it because I was mad at her."

"What dear?" my father wasn't following the conversation very closely; he was so preoccupied with the raw onion.

"I sent her the get well card," I said clearly, raising my voice to get his attention, "so she'd get well and go home."

My father stopped what he was doing, and looked at me. Then he jerked his head sideways as he heard a sound in the hall. My mother and aunt must have come in without our hearing them, because my aunt had just come down the hall to her room. Had she heard what I said? My father's eyes and mine mirrored the same question.

The next moment my mother came down the hall to the kitchen, saying, "Well, aren't you two the ones? Getting dinner all ready for us. I couldn't have done it myself. We're just completely worn out. There's nothing more tiring than a day downtown shopping."

My aunt was so tired, in fact, that she just had a light supper on a tray in her room that night.

On the day of her departure, the flat was a-bustle with last minute preparations: the hunting of a missing music case, looking for a bag that everyone had believed to be in the basement and so on. But at length, all of the bags were found, packed and were placed in the entry-hall ready to go.

Because of all the hustling and bustling, to get me out from underfoot my mother sent me out to sit on the front steps, and Margaret came along and sat with me.

"My aunt's leaving tonight," I told her.

"Bet you're glad."

"It'll sure be nice getting my bedroom back."

"Some relief, eh?"

"You said it."

"Gee, I thought you'd be all excited."

"I *am*."

"You don't sound it."

"Well I am."

"You almost sound sorry."

"Well I'm not. It's just that—oh nothing."

"What?"

"It's just that I sort of feel sorry for her."

"How come? When she was sick you didn't feel sorry for her. So how come you feel sorry for her when she's all better?"

"Well I don't think it was very nice of you to tell me to send her that card."

"You didn't hafta do it."

"It was a mean thing to do, and you were mean to suggest it."

"Well you were the one who did it."

"I wouldn't have done it if you hadn't said to."

"Well it got her to leave, didn't it?"

"I told you," I said, "the card didn't have anything to do with it. Well, maybe it had something to do with it, but it wasn't what got her to leave."

"Oh ya? Then what did?"

"It was her medicine and the Novena that made her better."

"Oh *sure*. My mother says it's Irish to believe in that stuff."

"That shows how much your mother knows."

"She knows a lot more than *your* mother."

"Oh ya? Well get off our property."

Margaret flounced off, and I went back into the flat.

My mother and sister were going to accompany my aunt to Bonaventure Station to put her on the train, but the rest of us gathered in the hall to say our good-byes.

My father had on his courtly, old-world manner, as he jokingly gave bits of advice to my aunt, and brushed aside her thanks for his hospitality. And when she thanked me for giving up my room, I mumbled, "Don't mention it." I might have tagged on, "It was nothing," but couldn't bring myself to go that far.

Finally the taxi arrived at the door. There was a flurry of last minute hugs and kisses and movement toward the door, when I said to my aunt, "Just a minute. I have something for you."

She turned toward me, looking surprised, and I thrust into her hand a piece of crumpled paper I had been folding and unfolding in indecision all through the good-byes.

She unfolded it and read it, then looked at me quizzically for an explanation. At my mother's questioning look she said, "It's an address and telephone number."

Everyone's attention focused on me. "It's your son's," I mumbled. "I just thought you might like to have it."

Everyone looked dumbfounded. My aunt seemed to go pale for a moment, my mother's mouth opened in astonishment, my father looked embarrassed, my sister and brothers looked uncomprehending, and I wished I hadn't brought the whole thing up. It wasn't the way it was in Shirley Temple movies at all. No one was smiling, and I didn't feel the least bit like dimpling and twinkling—the way Shirley did when she reunited Alice Faye and Jack Haley in "Poor Little Rich Girl."

My mother was the first to find her voice, "Where in the world. . . ."

"Margaret and I found it downtown in a Winnipeg phone book," I said.

My mother looked at my aunt for her reaction, and my aunt smiled.

"Why, thank you, dear, very much. It's the very nicest present. I may never use it, but, as you say, it will be nice to know I have it."

The taxi horn honked, my father took his watch out of his vest pocket for a final check, and in another little flurry they were gone.

I watched from the living-room window as they went down the steps. My aunt walked with her shoulders back and her chin held high, and I saw her gently shrug off my mother's unconsciously helping hand. I saw them get settled in the cab, and my aunt lift her hand in a wave as the cab turned in the driveway before making its way up the street, then, letting the curtain fall back into place, I went down the hall to the vacated bedroom. I hadn't remembered it being so small.

I sat down on the freshly-made bed and gave a tentative bounce, to test its springiness. When it bounced back, I bounced a little harder. In a few moments I was bouncing as high as I could go, and could feel my bangs lifting as I came down hard on the bed, then went up again.

My father, who was on his way down the hall to the kitchen, paused in the doorway to watch this display of high spirits, and smiled.

I was beginning to get breathless as I bounced higher and higher, laughing at my own exuberance. When I stopped at last, my father said, "Well, you've got your room back." And I nodded, still breathless, as he quoted:

The lark's on the wing;
The snail's on the thorn
God's in his heaven—
All's right with the world!

I grinned in agreement, and he continued down the hall.